CW00400320

The Craft Brewers' Compendium

An omnibus of brewing materials

Ted Bruning
with Technical Editor
Don Burgess

i

First published in Great Britain 2017 by
Posthouse Publishing Ltd, No 2 Cleat, St Margaret's Hope, South Ronaldsay,
Orkney, KW17 2RW.
© Ted Bruning & Posthouse Publishing

A CIP catalogue for this book is available from the British Library
ISBN 978 1 90387235 2

10 9 8 7 6 5 4 3 2 1

All rights reserved. No part of this publication may be reproduced, stored in a
retrieval system or transmitted in any form, or by any means, electronic or mechanical,
including photocopying and recording, or by any information storage and retrieval system except as may be expressly permitted by the UK 1988 Copyright, Designs and Patents
Act and the USA 1976 Copyright Act or in writing from the publisher. Requests for
permission should be addressed to Posthouse Publishing Ltd, No 2 Cleat, St Margaret's
Hope, South Ronaldsay, Orkney, KW17 2RW.

Disclaimer: The publishers have made every effort to ensure the accuracy of information
in the book at the time of going to press. However, they cannot accept responsibility for any
loss, injury or inconvenience resulting from the use of information contained in this book.

Printed and bound in Great Britain by T.J. Internatonal Ltd.

Contents

Getting Technical

Dedication

This book is respectfully dedicated to Martin Sykes and Basil Savage, founders of Selby Brewery in Yorkshire, England, in 1972. Selby, which ceased brewing in 1998, was the first fully commercial microbrewery in Britain and hence the world. Without Martin and Basil's pioneering vision and leadership there would be no microbrewing and no craft brewing today; and few of the ingredients in this book would even have been thought of.

Foreword

It's with great pleasure that I write this foreword to what I regard as one of the most useful books to appear on the small-scale brewing scene in recent years.

In 2015, Ted Bruning and I co-wrote Wisdom for Home Brewers. Since then we have seen more beer styles develop, New England IPAs, Kettle Sours and Double Brett IPAs among them. According to one source there are now more than 150 defined styles. The opportunity to enhance and develop existing styles, create new styles and brewing techniques has never been greater in my opinion. It is truly an exciting time in the beer world.

The range of hops available now exceeds 260 varieties, with ongoing breeding programmes looking particularly for intense aromatic qualities, so we can have lemon to lychee and pineapple to papaya in our aromas and flavours. Indeed, for a number of years beers became very hop-focused that led, perhaps, to a rather one-dimensional arena in terms of flavour; but there is now greater interest in other methods of adding or enhancing beer flavour.

The range of malts and adjuncts open to us brewers also offers even more flexibility now, and much of the former stigma of using adjuncts has disappeared. Adjuncts, and I use the term in its widest sense, offer a new world of colours and flavours whether they be fruit juices, herbs, spices or botanicals. Who would have thought, even five years ago, that we would be looking at agave nectar and jaggery in our brews?

We now have a wider range of fermentation organisms to use, too, including many that were originally confined to traditional beer styles such as lambic and the like. We can even shorten these beers' two–three year traditional fermentation and maturation periods to 12 hours using a blend of lactobacillus strains as in kettle sours. We can then use Brettanomyces for 'funky' attributes: once the bane of many brewers, we now welcome it with open arms!

In this book Ted has given a useful reference point for all the main ingredients, so it's a book to be used, not parked on a shelf. In addition we have the contribution of Don Burgess as technical editor. Don is a former colleague of mine at SIBA (the Society of Independent Brewers) here in the UK where he was technical director. His practical knowledge of craft brewing is immense in both depth and breadth.

All in all, this is a most useful addition to the craft brewer's library and one that will no doubt prove particularly useful when it comes to recipe formulation and as a quick handy reference point.

Enjoy!

Nigel Sadler
Director, Learn2brew Ltd
IBD Accredited Trainer
Vice-Chairman IBD (UK Southern Section)
Cask Marque Assessor
Beer Academy Tutor
APPBG Beer Sommelier of the Year 2012

Author's Preface

This book is an attempt to uncover as many brewing ingredients and materials as I could and present them in as practical a format as possible, and compiling it has been fascinating and not without its challenges.

Readers may find it ironic that the compilation of a printed catalogue should have relied so little on printed sources. In fact only two books have played much of a part in creating this compendium: *Culpeper's Complete Herbal* by Nicholas Culpeper and John J Palmer's indispensable *How To Brew* (Brewers Publications 2006). The rest has been mainly a long search of the internet.

I started by blithely rifling the online sales catalogues of maltsters, hop merchants and yeast laboratories and quickly made two discoveries. The first was something I knew already: that most companies carry broadly similar ranges, which for reasons of space I have had to whittle into representative listings that should allow you to shop around with a clear underlying idea of what you want and can reasonably expect to find.

The second and rather more time-consuming challenge was something I also knew already but had perhaps underestimated: that sales catalogues don't share a standard format and that each company has its own idea of what data its customers will find useful. This has involved me in searching for hard data on the websites of institutes and organisations such as the, United States Department of Agriculture (USDA) and for background information on the many online forums and news groups shared by home brewers, whose innovative spirit and eagerness to share was both exhilarating and inspirational.

If, in selecting from the many categories of malt, I allowed myself to exercise my judgment, the opposite was true of hops. Here my aim was to be as encyclopaedic as humanly possible, and I succeeded in rounding up more than 300 strains from around the world. However there were significant gaps: for instance, I identified 21 native strains from the districts of Ukraine that used to be the Soviet Union's principal hop-growing region; but as the strategy of the country's largest growers is to produce popular international lager varieties at low cost for export, information about native varieties seems impossible to get. In Lithuania half-a-dozen native strains, no longer cultivated, are kept in a plant archive; but dozens of traditional pub-breweries survive using wild hops foraged from the neighbouring hedgerows, which are of course completely undocumented. Then again China is thought to be the ancestral home of both humulus lupulus and humulusyunnanensis, of which hundreds of species grow wild, but it has only a handful of commercially grown brewing strains of its own, about which almost no data is readily available.

Eventually my internet foraging led me to the marvellous The Hops List, a catalogue of 265 varieties compiled by the American home-brewer and researcher Julian Healey. Had I discovered The Hops List earlier I might have been less assiduous in my researches than he was, which would have been a shame because I did uncover a few varieties he doesn't feature, and I have also discarded a few of his selections as not really being different enough to warrant a full listing. The real reason, though, why every home and craft brewer should possess a copy – either print or digital – of The Hops List is that Julian has been able to go into much greater detail than I could hope to find space for. Not only does he include basic agronomical detail for the swelling ranks of brewers who choose to grow their own, he has also researched testimonials from home and craft brewers with practical experience of using the varieties he lists.

For my listings of different yeast strains I returned to sales catalogues, in the knowledge that an encyclopaedic listing was impossible but still hoping to present a broad enough spectrum to cover most of the brewer's needs. I finally stopped, exhausted, at 128, knowing full well that I could have carried on but also becoming aware that there is necessarily overlap to the point of duplication. I hope that I have given you your fill.

My particular thanks are due to my technical editor Don Burgess, who has stopped many a howler slipping through the net, and also to Charlie Gorham of Charles Faram Ltd and Dr Peter Darby of Wye Hops.

Introduction

How would Cézanne have seen Mont Sainte-Victoire if he had had an infinite palette? God knows how often he painted it, and always in different moods; but who knows how much more often, and in how many more moods, he might have painted it if only he had had more colours – if he had had access to digital graphic design software, say?

In our combined 65 years of commenting on and participating in what used to be called microbrewing, Don Burgess and I have seen the palette of flavours and ingredients available to the brewer multiply exponentially. The gulf between what was available in the 1980s and what is available now, especially in terms of hops, is as great as the gulf between Cézanne's palette and the infinite gradations of colour to which a digital artist has access. And this very breadth of potential has, in itself, had a transformative effect. Old beer styles have been revived; current beer styles have been nuanced and inflected; entirely new beer styles have emerged. As a consequence, thousands upon thousands of newcomers across the globe have been lured by the magic of the mash tun, some amateur, some professional, but each and every one of them an explorer on an unknown ocean.

But every silver lining has its cloud, and in this case it's that the charts that once guided intrepid brewer-mariners reliably around the seven seas of beer are all out of date. Your choice of materials is no longer limited to what is available locally. Thanks to e-commerce, a cornucopia of malts, adjuncts, sugars, hops, flavourings, yeasts and bacterial cultures from all round the world can be yours almost wherever you are; and thanks to growing and ever more sophisticated demand the list of options is getting longer and longer. And yet nowhere is there one single superstore where you can browse everything on the market.

The information you need is out there all right, but it's scattered across websites, sales catalogues, magazines, even books! And it's hard to focus on a new recipe or an improvement on an old one or just a different combination of yeasts when you're continually jumping from site to site, scrolling up and down, bookmarking anything you think you like the look of and checking back to cross-reference... Your train of thought is constantly being interrupted – it's like playing Chinese whispers with yourself.

That's where this book comes in. It is, as it describes itself, a compendium – an attempt to round up and present as many nuggets of information as it can. It concentrates almost exclusively on ingredients and process aids on the premise that you know better than anyone what to do with them once you've found them: this is emphatically not a 'how to brew book.' There's nothing in it that you couldn't have found elsewhere – in fact, it contains not a scrap of new information. But here, between these two covers, you'll find more than 500 entries covering the entire spectrum from brewing liquor to cask finings, all described in manageable chunks that you can either browse in serendipitous hope or simply use as reference material.

From all this, the question naturally arises: why go to print at all, when a website has such clear advantages in terms of day-to-day utility? To which our reply is that it doesn't. Speaking as researchers who spend most of our working days with our noses buried either in a computer or a book we have concluded that a book has one enormous advantage over a screen, which is that you can riffle it. It's a simple fact that flicking back and forth in a physical book is much quicker than scrolling up and down a screen, and that actual bookmarks are far quicker to use than digital ones. In addition to that, if you take a book into the brewery and it gets splashed with hot sticky wort, it will still be more or less decipherable. Try that with a laptop and... well, good luck with the insurance claim!

But there's another attribute a book possesses that a website doesn't, one that is perhaps even more important than utility, and that's pleasure. Nobody ever curled up for the evening with a bottle or two of beer and a good computer. We sincerely hope that this book is of practical value to you in your brewing. We also hope, every bit as sincerely, that you enjoy it.

PART ONE

Welcome to the mash tun

1: Malt

Malt is, of course, the building block of the beer, providing the fermentable materials that create the alcohol, the residual sugars that create the mouthfeel, and the warm, grainy, biscuity flavour components. In particular it's pale malts of various types, principally lager malt, pale ale malt and wheat malt, kilned at low temperature to preserve the golden colour of the grain, that are the platforms on which nearly all modern beers are founded. The grists of even the blackest of beers usually have pale malts as their main constituents, the colour being supplied by small doses of darker types. Low-temperature drying preserves amylase, the saccharifying enzyme in the malt, as well as its original colour. This means that the malt can be used with other unmalted grains such as wheat, corn and rice, supplementing their lack of amylase with its own.

Readers of this book will already be more than familiar with the malting process – they'll be intimate with it. They'll plan grists blended from all shades and flavours of malt from white wheat to patent black. They'll choose, when they can, malt made from heritage varieties of barley such as Plumage Archer, Chevallier and, of course, Maris Otter, all locally-sourced, fully traceable and traditionally floor-malted. And when the number of different types of malt on the market is multiplied by the number of brewing sugars and adjuncts, and then by the various different types of hops and other flavourings, the vocabulary and inflections available to home and craft brewer alike become almost infinite.

For the sake of utility, the malts listed here are classified by colour, expressed somewhat quaintly (some will think) as degrees Lovibond, a system that although hardly used any more is at least understood throughout the English-speaking brewing world. The more accurate and up-to-date methods – Standard Reference Measure in most countries and the European Brewing Convention scale in the EU – use blue light to measure the colour of laboratory worts under test conditions, whereas Lovibond measures the colour of the malted grains by visual comparison with coloured glass discs. Lovibond might, therefore, be of more use than the other methods to smaller brewers buying malt.

The potential percentage of fermentable sugars is also given in the case of the main base malts. The values given are not exact since practices and procedures vary from maltster to maltster, but they should give the brewer a clear idea of what to expect.

Acidulated malt aka Sour malt, Sauermalz (2-3°L): contains 1-2 per cent lactic acid, lowers the mash's pH and provides a rounder, fuller character, enhancing the flavour of Pilsners and other light lagers. In larger quantities it adds a refreshing sourness. Lowering the pH also helps prevent oxidisation. Self-converting.

Amber malt (30°L): similar to Mild Ale or Vienna malt, but with more colour and a biscuity flavour. Amber malt is a more toasted version of Pale Ale malt, kilned at temperatures of 150-160C. Its slightly bitter flavour mellows with age. Non-diastatic.

Aromatic malt (20°L): an American equivalent to Munich malt, which in small additions (up to 10 per cent) will intensify the malt character of a lightly flavoured beer. Kilned at 115°C. Self-converting.

Belgian Pale Ale malt (3°L; 80.5%): generally darker than its British and American equivalents as it is kilned for longer but at a lower temperature. Fully diastatic.

Biscuit malt (25°L): lightly roasted malt used to darken some Belgian beers and create a toasty, biscuity flavour; typically used as 10 per cent of the total grain bill. Gives a deep amber colour to the beer. Fully diastatic.

MALT

Black malt aka Patent malt (5-600°L): this is as dark as malt can get, having been kilned at 200C to the point of carbonisation. Consequently it has a very strong burnt wood flavour and must be used very sparingly, generally less than 250g per 25l. Debittered or husked black malt has less of the burnt-wood bitterness. The term 'patent malt' comes from its invention in 1817 by English maltster Daniel Wheeler. Non-diastatic.

Brown malt (65°L): traditionally kilned over a wood fire for a lightly smoky flavour; used very sparingly in brown ales, stouts and porters. Non-diastatic.

Brumalt: *see* Gambrinus Honey malt.

Carafa I, II, III (300-600°L): roughly speaking, Germany's equivalent of Chocolate and Coffee malts. Pitch-black, they produce flavours and aromas of chocolate and coffee along with a very mild bitterness. Non-diastatic.

Caramel/Crystal malts ie Carapils, Caravienne, Carahell (10-120°L): grains that after germination aren't dried in the usual way but are further heated or 'stewed' at high temperature while still damp. Finally they are roasted for colour, and as the process destroys all their enzymes they have no diastatic power. At the same time their sugars mostly crystallise, then caramelise in the mashtun and become unfermentable. This results in sweeter, fuller and darker beers, often with a strong flavour of toffee, although if too much is used an undesirably astringent taste becomes noticeable. Caramel or Crystal malts of different colours and under different names are widely used across the brewing world: in Britain and America they are graded according to degrees

Lovibond, i.e.Caramel (or Crystal) 10, 40, 60, 80, 120; in Germany and other European countries they are named after the beers to which they are thought most suited, i.e. Carapils,Caravienne, Carahell and Caramunch. Carapils is sometimes also called Dextrin malt. Non-diastatic.

Chocolate malt (350-400°L): similar to pale and amber malts but kilned at even higher temperatures. Its smooth bitter-sweet chocolate flavour, roasty bitterness and brown-ish-black colour with ruby highlights make chocolate malt irreplaceable in dark ales such as milds, stouts and porters; it can also be used in dark lagers and in lesser amounts in brown ale. Non-diastatic.

Coffee malt (150°L): halfway between Brown malt and Choc-olate malt, Coffee malt imparts the smooth richness of the one and the colour of the other but without any of the bitter-ness. And its flavour and aroma are surprisingly close to… well, coffee! Non-diastatic.

Distiller's malt (2-3°L; 80.5%): standard Distiller's or Pot-still malt is quite light and very high in nitrogen compared to beer malts. Since whisky distillers are well aware that it's not beer they're producing, the malts they use are bred for maximum efficiency both in terms of their extraction of fermentable sugars and their speed of fermentation. Distiller's malt there-fore features a high nitrogen content to keep the yeast well-fed and exceptional diastatic power, which enables the brewer to experiment with a high proportion of unmalted grains. Fully diastatic.

GambrinusHoneymaltakaHoneymaltakaBrumalt(18-20°L): in-tenselyflavoured,lightlycolouredmaltwithaslightlynuttytaste

M
A
L
T

that enriches and rounds out a beer, rather like Aromatic malt. Made by a process very similar to Caramel/Crystal malt. Self-converting.

Lager malt aka Pilsner malt (2°L; 80%): the malt that makes the world's most popular beer style can also be used as the foundation for other beers, even dark ales. Its diastatic capability, or ability to convert starch into sugar, makes it ideal for use with low-enzyme speciality malts or unmalted grains. Its natural flavour is discreetly earthy with some sweetness. It's also the palest commonly available base malt, and for all these reasons makes an incomparably versatile platform for your experiments or, if you prefer, flights of fancy. Lager malt extract will also make a quick and fairly neutral base beer for your hop trials. Fully diastatic.

Melanoidin (25°L): melanoid is the colour compound produced by cooking at a medium heat of around 140-165C – it's the golden-brown on the crust of a loaf and the darker brown of a roast leg of lamb produced by the Maillard reaction. When malt is kilned in the correct temperature range it too is coloured by melanoids, which also produce a round flavour and mouthfeel with a comparably small addition to the mash. Usually used in amber lagers and ales, dark lagers and Scottish and red ales. Non-diastatic.

Mild Ale malt (4°L; 79%): Although most milds are dark the base malt isn't, creating an amber wort to which brown, chocolate and/or black malts are added sparingly to create the characteristic colour. Mild Ale malt is also a good platform for stronger ales, whether coloured or not. It's kilned at slightly higher temperatures than pale malt to provide the rounder flavour commonly described as 'nutty'. Fully diastatic.

Munich malt (5-10°L; 79%): an aromatic lager malt that yields a dark reddish-orange wort and a slightly sweet caramel flavour. Munich malt comes in two grades, light and dark. The light version is fully diastatic and is the base malt of most bocks, especially doppelbock, and in smaller quantities provides the sweeter, maltier undertones in Dunkels and Mäerzens. The dark version is self-converting.

Oat malt (4°L): unmalted oats have long been a very popular brewing adjunct principally because their high husk content cleans up a beer and produces a velvety smooth texture especially prized in stouts and Scotch ales. It has traditionally been seen as gilding the lily to go to the effort and expense of malting the grains and as a result oat malt has become a rarity. Recent research, though, has demonstrated that it is perfectly possible to brew a 100 per cent oat malt beer the equal of barley malt beer in every way except one: extraction is only three-quarters as efficient, which may very well be why brewing with oat malt died out in the first place. But oat beer has one huge and potentially lucrative advantage: trials in several countries have shown that most sufferers from gluten intolerance can safely enjoy oat products including beer brewed with oat malt. Fully diastatic.

Pale Ale malt (3°L; 80.5%): the malt most commonly associated with British ale is kilned at 95-105C, a slightly higher temperature than lager malt, for a fuller flavour and darker colour. As well as being the base malt for British beers from bitter to stout, it's the precursor in the production of most other British malts. Pale Ale malt is derived from both two-row and six-row barley; the latter is higher in nitrogen and is therefore a source of yeast nutrient. Fully diastatic.

Peated malt (3ºL): distiller's malt that has been dried over peat, which imparts the smoky aroma and flavour associated with some Islay whiskies. Brewers have recently and mistakenly included peated malt in interpretations of Scotch ales, which actually are industrially-brewed, sweet, low-hop mild ales. When peat is used liberally in brewing, the result tends to be a very strong earthy and smoky flavour. Fully diastatic.

Rauchmalz (3ºL): dried over an open fire, usually of beech chips, rather than in a kiln, Rauchmalz has a smoky aroma and is the distinctive peaty/iodine flavour in Rauchbier. Used sparingly, it can give strong dark beers an interesting twist. (Alder-smoked malt is used in Alaskan smoked porter.) Rauchmalz comes in several varieties, generally corresponding to standard kilned varieties (e.g. Rauchpilsner to Pilsner); the colour and diastatic power of each variety are equal to those of the equivalent kilned grain.

Rice malt: *see* Rice Syrup.

Rostmalz (300-500ºL): ranging from chocolate to black, these German roasted malts are generally smoother and less bitter than their UK/US counterparts.

Rye malt (3ºL; 80%): a 10-20 per cent addition of malted rye should be ample to create that characteristic dry, grainy, slightly spicy flavour; a German-style Roggenbier will contain around 35 per cent. But have a care: with no hulls of its own and a high beta-glucan content, it can be very sticky in the mash. A dose of oat or rice hulls makes a useful process aid along with beta-glucanase if using higher percentages; a mashing temperature a degree or two higher than the norm should stop it setting. A longer sparging time is also part of the rye package. Self-converting. A very dark version, Chocolate Rye malt (250°L), is the height of sophistication in a velvety yet spicy last-thing-at-night strong ale. Non-diastatic.

Six-row Pale malt (2°L; 80.5%): nitrogen and enzyme-rich malt used as a base for rapid and thorough conversion in the mash, as well as for extra body and fullness; the flavour is more neutral than standard two-row malts. Fully diastatic.

Special Belgian malt (220°L): a rare malt with a nutty, roasted sweetness that in small quantities enriches brown ales and porters, and in larger proportions adds a plummy, vinous quality to barley wines and strong winter beers. Non-diastatic.

Special Roast malt (50°L): a darker variety of Victory malt. Creates a very attractive deep golden-brown colour and a rich biscuity flavour. In small additions gives depth and complexity to IPAs, Mäerzens and bocks. Non-diastatic.

Spelt Saison malt (2-3°L, 79%): a hard-hulled heirloom wheat, more proteinaceous than other malts. The saison grade is suitable for witbiers as well as saisons and brings sweet and nutty flavours, a well-rounded body and a spicy aroma. Weyermann, Briess and others kiln spelt across the range from pale to black.

Stout malt (2ºL; 80.5%): specialist base malt for stout, gently kilned (and consequently light in colour) for maximum diastatic power to convert the large proportions of dark malts and unmalted grain required as thoroughly as possible. Now rare. Fully diastatic.

Toasted Pale malt (25ºL): often made at home by toasting common-or-garden pale malt for 10-15 minutes at 180C for use as a handy substitute for commercially-made Biscuit or Victory malt. Non-diastatic.

Victory malt (25ºL): US roasted malt similar to Biscuit but with a nuttier taste. Adds pale copper highlights to the beer colour. Non-diastatic.

Vienna malt (4ºL; 79%): lighter and sweeter than Munich malt and the principal ingredient in bock beers. Produces the full-bodied amber or reddish beers that were once popular in Austria but survive mainly in Mexico, with Dos Equis and Negra Modelo being noted modern examples. Self-converting.

Wheat malt (2ºL; 80%): wheat has been used in brewing for nearly as long as barley but has always played second fiddle for a number of reasons, not least because it makes better bread than barley and has therefore tended to be reserved for baking. In brewing terms its lack of a husk means that even though it has all barley's diastatic power, it has traditionally had to be mashed with at least 30 per cent barley malt. (In the modern world of high-tech milling rice hulls will do the job just as well, but that wasn't an option open to our forefathers.) Its high protein content not only leads to a hazy wort but, worse, can create a stuck mash. Nevertheless its distinctive flavours and refreshingly light body have made wheat beers a perennial favourite over the centuries, especially among manual workers who needed both a high-calorie diet and thorough rehydration at the end of the working day. Dark Wheat malt (7ºL) creates a golden colour and a richer, creamier mouthfeel. White Wheat malt (1.5ºL) is made from a different strain of wheat that is even higher in protein and will therefore generate an even more opaque haze. All are fully diastatic. Carawheat (45ºL) is a great flavour intensifier for a dark lager or wheat beer, while a judicious addition of Chocolate Wheat malt (400ºL) can transform an everyday wheat beer into a wheat stout. Both non-diastatic.

2: Unmalted Grains

Not all brewing grains need to be malted. Up to 50 per cent of the grist of a Belgian witbier is unmalted wheat, but the malted barley that makes up the rest has enough enzymes to convert the whole mash. Unmalted oats are added to some beers, especially stout, for their husky roughness, which scrubs microscopic particles out of the wort for a silky smooth finish. Maize and rice are almost flavourless but are high in convertible starch. They have no enzymes of their own, but as with Belgian wheat beer, the barley malts they are mashed with have enough enzymes for the whole mash. Finally, roasted barley is virtually burnt to an inky black 550ºL and has an acrid charred-wood flavour that is the signature of Irish stouts.

> **Black barley (525ºL):** like roasted barley but even darker, and with a strong burnt-wood astringency. Used to create dryness in stouts and porters.

Flaked barley (1.5ºL): unmalted barley is often used in stouts to provide protein for head retention and to round out the body and mouthfeel. It can also be used in other strong ale styles. Flaked grains are dried and rolled flat and may also be 'torrefied' – cooked at 220-300C in a sealed low-oxygen environment to drive off moisture and volatiles – in which case it will be high in haze-producing proteins.

Flaked maize (1ºL): once used extensively to lighten American ales, which were brewed with high-protein six-row barley. More recently used as cheap sources of flavourless fermentable sugars in light lagers, although today corn grits are more common. Often added sparingly to lighten the body of some strong Belgian beers that would otherwise be overweight and cloying, and a common adjunct in British bitters and milds for the same reason.

Flaked rice (1ºL): flavourless adjunct used in American and Japanese light lagers. Can be as much as 40 per cent of the mash. Technically speaking, as rice is a cereal not a fruit and as its starches therefore have to be converted by mashing in hot water, saki and other Oriental rice 'wines' are actually beers.

Flaked wheat (2ºL): unmalted wheat is sharper tasting than malted wheat and is therefore a common ingredient in American, Bavarian and Belgian wheat beers. Its complex carbohydrates are essential to the wild yeasts and bacteria that ferment Belgian lambics, while its high protein level can create an almost milky haze.

Grits (1-1.5ºL): dried, roughly ground and cooked maize kernels that will lighten the body, stretch the malt and dilute the protein haze in a beer.

Oats (1ºL): unmalted oats lend a silky, creamy mouthfeel to a stout that counteracts the harshness of black malt and roasted barley. They are available whole, steel-cut, rolled and flaked. Rolled and flaked oats have been cooked to gelatinise (make soluble) their starches and are sold as instant oatmeal in every supermarket. They need to be cooked according to the instructions on the packet (but with more water) to ensure that the starches will be fully converted and need to be mashed with barley malt. Rolled or steel-cut oats (oat grits) are used as mash ingredients in oatmeal stout. Gluten free.

Roasted barley (300ºL): toasted until almost black, but well short of incineration, roasted barley usually makes up the biggest component of stout after the base malt itself. It contributes the dark brown colour and ruby highlights and also the characteristic rich, sweetish, coffee-ish flavour.

Rye (2ºL): unmalted rye imparts a dry, spicy flavour but can create same problems in the mashtun as it does when malted.

Torrefied wheat (2ºL): raw wheat that has been cooked at 220-300C in a closed low-oxygen oven to drive off moisture and volatiles. Used to enhance head formation and retention.

3: Brewing Sugars

Our ancestors probably didn't realise it, but their primitive ale-brewing was in fact nothing less than the manipulation of enzymes and other microorganisms to convert insoluble starches into soluble sugars and hence into alcohol – a sophisticated feat of biochemical engineering that they performed every day without the slightest awareness of what they were doing.

BREWING SUGARS

But if this quotidian miracle is central to the art of science of brewing – is the art and science of brewing, you might well say – it's not the end of sugar's role in the process. For the use of sugar in brewing is widespread throughout the world. Some beer-lovers claim that its only role is to pad out expensive malt with a much cheaper source of fermentable material, and in some cases this may have some basis in fact. American brewers in particular use large amounts of rice or corn-based syrups to produce the very light-bodied, pale beers their consumers favour – but which came first, the customer preference or the light-bodied beer, is not the subject of this work.

There are other less controversial and indeed time-honoured uses for various types of sugar in judicious quantities. Small amounts are often used to iron out inconsistencies of strength and colour between mashes, and to prime bottles and casks to trigger a secondary fermentation that enhances the beer's condition and head. Larger amounts will boost alcoholic volume without affecting flavour. Finally, specialist sugars may be added at different stages for their distinctive flavour characteristics. Used wisely, they add another layer, another dimension.

Agave nectar: various agave cacti have been cultivated throughout Mesoamerica for centuries for their fleshy hearts and sugary juice. Left to itself the juice will be spontaneously fermented by bacteria, not yeast, to make a sour, moderately alcoholic beverage called pulque. The cooked hearts yield a fermentable syrup that is the base of mezcal, which is both a beverage in its own right and the precursor of tequila. If the juice is reduced over heat before it starts fermenting it will condense into a fairly neutral syrup very high in fructose and glucose, which brewers use to help ensure a fast, reliable fermentation.

Birch sap: a traditional staple in brewing all over northern Russia, Scandinavia and the Baltic States as well as Canada and Alaska, birch sap is interesting stuff. Straight from the tree it's very watery, with only a suggestion of sweetness; in fact it's a potent cocktail of enzymes, minerals, proteins, antioxidants, vitamins and all those obscure micronutrients that make a health shop manager's eyes light up. Unfortunately for the brewer its sugar content is a mere 0.5-2 per cent, so it takes a fair bit of boiling down to make a syrup comparable to maple (see below). But if you go out in early spring, when the birch is in bud but before it's in leaf, and tap a few trees (mature ones, please – the process is invasive!) you should get enough sap to make not a brewing sugar but a brewing liquor. (And always plug the drill-hole after tapping, or it will become infected.) You can reduce the sap a bit to concentrate it slightly and kill off the bugs, which will include wild yeasts of uncertain character. Used with lager malt or pale malt it will confer a sweet-and-sour character a bit like balsamic vinegar and also a weissbiery bubblegum flavour thanks to the presence of xylitol, a naturally sweet alcohol derived from xylose.

Brown rice syrup aka rice malt syrup, rice syrup: traditionally made by boiling unpolished brown rice with enough malted barley to convert its starches to fermentable sugar, and then concentrated by boiling; now more likely to be synthesised. Used in bulk to lighten and strengthen mass-produced lagers.

Brown sugar: whether straightforward white sugar crystals coated with a little molasses or a portion extracted and crystallised halfway through the refining stage, brown sugar is pure sucrose that will easily be broken down by the yeast's own invertase during primary or secondary fermentation. As well as modifying the alcoholic strength of your beer it brings with it a very faint rummy flavour. If using brown sugar for priming, store the bottles at room temperature for a few days to let the invertase do its work before moving them out to the chill of the garage.

Candi: sucrose solution heated slowly with acid (normally citric) until it condenses and crystallises, during which it inverts or splits into fermentable glucose and fructose. Widely used in Belgium either in pale form to lighten a beer's body without affecting its gravity (like corn syrup) or, heated until it caramelises slightly, to darken the beer and add a little extra flavour. Also, being very pure it makes for a faster primary fermentation.

Corn syrup: slightly diluted starch-derived dextrose monohydrate (a variant of glucose). Flavourless; boosts alcohol and makes for a faster fermentation; also used for priming. Corn-derived and therefore gluten-free in the US; wheat-derived in Europe and may contain gluten at trace level.

Demerara aka Turbinado sugar: crystallised at an early stage in the sugarcane refining process, Demerara or Turbinado comes as pale brown crunchy crystals that give a warm caramel flavour.

Dextrose: *see* Corn Syrup.

Golden syrup: developed in the late 19th century by Abram Lyle of Tate & Lyle fame as a way of utilising dross discarded during the refining process, Golden Syrup is an invert sugar and therefore fully fermentable. The inversion process, which involves the use of hydrochloric acid, creates both the beautiful dark gold colour and the characteristic warm, rich, ever-so-slightly salty flavour. Recycled waste products never tasted so good!

Honey: modern consensus has it that honey holds the honour of being the source of the world's oldest alcoholic drink (an honour it possibly shares with palm sap). As well as being the precursor of mead, it also has an honourable place in the history of brewing: the medieval Welsh, for instance, brewed a beer called braggot whose mash was up to two-thirds honey and which was infused with costly imported spices – a luxury liquor for the most affluent in society.

Honey is a very versatile and characterful substance, just stuffed with substances the brewer finds invaluable. Its sugars are mainly fructose and glucose, easily accessible to yeast, but it also contains amylase to help convert the more complex sugars and starches in other ingredients. The range of flavours contained in that one little five-letter word is simply staggering – from acacia honey as pale and elegant as a fino sherry to buckwheat honey as dark and robust as a vintage port.

One caveat is that as honey is typically less than 20 per cent water it can contain in a state of suspended animation a viable population of harmful microorganisms; and since honey is not normally introduced to the beer until secondary fermentation there is a real risk that they will come back to life and cause some pretty nasty diseases. Brewers should therefore only use pasteurised honey; if your brewing honey is raw, cook it for half an hour at 80C in a bain-marie before use. An addition of up to 10 per cent to light ales and lagers will create subtle, teasing flavours and aromas. Additions of up to 30 per cent will need to be balanced by stronger hops, Caramel/Crystal or even roasted malts, and possibly spices too. At between 30-66 per cent honey its flavour will dominate the beer; above that and you have not beer but mead.

Invert sugar: beet sugar has an undesirable flavour that can be avoided by 'inverting' it – boiling it slowly with water and citric acid down to a concentrated syrup that is crystallised to form sugar 'diamonds'. It has a faint but distinctive after-taste that lovers of Belgian abbey beers will recognise and savour.

Jaggery: a newcomer and still a rarity as a brewing sugar, jaggery is the southern hemisphere's equivalent of maple syrup. Traditionally it's simply palm sap, reduced to a (rather sticky) solid in shallow open pans, formed into blocks and left to dry in the sun. In modern times as the oil palms have been felled and not replanted, sugarcane sap has been used either to bulk out the palm sap or, increasingly, to replace it entirely. The true palm-derived version can be anything from tan to nearly black; it tends to be (very roughly) 50 per cent sucrose, 20 per cent simple sugars, 20 per cent moisture and 10 per cent whatever happened to be flying around during the hours it was reducing (a lot of it being ash from the fire it was dried over). Used in the boil at a ratio by weight of not more than one part in six it lightens the body of the beer but also brings a combination of rich flavours – dark chocolate, caramel, salt and even (according to one taster) butter.

Lactose: non-fermentable milk sugar that can be added at any stage to sweeten and augment body to a dry beer, especially a stout (although a stout enriched with lactose can no longer legally be sold as a 'milk stout' in the UK, whether or not it 'looks good, it tastes good and by golly it does you good'). Actually it's misleading to say that lactose can't be fermented because in Central Asia it's the basis of koumiss, a not terribly alcoholic sour 'beer' that can then be distilled into arak. And in Dorset, England, excess whey from the UK dairy industry is used to make Black Cow Vodka. The responsible micro-organism here, though, isn't brewer's yeast but Kluyveromyces marxianus.

Maltodextrin: Maltodextrin is a non-fermentable starch that creates a heavier body and richer mouthfeel and aids head retention. In America it's normally corn-derived, but in Europe it's wheat-derived and may therefore contain traces of gluten. The chief ingredient in the artificial sweetener sucralose.

Maple syrup: creates complex flavours of coffee, vanilla, caramel, wood and smoke. If you're lucky enough to live in Canada, you can enhance the character still further by using the sap as brewing liquor. Use a complementary reddish-brown base malt such as Mild, Munich or even Biscuit to maintain that wonderful colour, but treat maple syrup very carefully: its aromatics are unusually volatile and will easily evaporate. Use it as a secondary addition, and keep the fermentation temperature down as low as you dare.

Molasses: the sticky black dross left over after the sugarcane refining process, molasses or black treacle is incredibly rich in all sorts of nutrients and flavours and is composed of up to 50 per cent residual sugar, two-thirds of it sucrose and the rest mostly glucose and fructose. Added judiciously to stouts, barley wines and old ales during the boil it creates

B
R
E
W
I
N
G

S
U
G
A
R
S

great density and depth of flavour, with a warm dark rum/treacle toffee aroma and a lovely lingering mouthcoating.

Muscovado: very strongly flavoured, moist, dark-brown almost unrefined sugar as much at home in savoury dishes as in sweet. Mineral-rich. Used as molasses but added just after the boil, it has very similar characteristics.

Rice syrup: *see* Brown Rice Syrup.

Sorbitol: actually an alcohol that is both tasteless and power-fully sweet. It occurs naturally in pears and is particularly favoured by hard cidermakers whose products are a tad dry for most consumers. Bear in mind that in anything more than tiny doses it's a highly effective laxative.

Stevia: Stevia rebaudiana extract is an incredibly powerful sweetener, but some brewers complain that it has a bitter aftertaste although it must be said that others disagree. Only permitted in the US in 2008 and by the EU in 2011 thanks to cancer fears. Non-fermentable; adds only sweetness and not body.

4: Mashed Vegetables

However insatiable the craft brewing movement's curiosity and thirst for novelty, it seems somehow unlikely that vegetable beer might ever be the next fruit beer. Home winemakers, it's true, can wrest a potable alcoholic beverage out of almost any vegetable matter from nettles to carrots; substitute LME for white sugar and there's no obstacle to any brewer doing the same – indeed, the Kitchen Brewery in Hudders-field, West Yorkshire (1996–2001), produced almost nothing else. The question is, though: why would you?

Well, not primarily for flavour. Few vegetables have distinctive enough flavours to outcompete the more established aromatics. Celery is one: a celery beer with perhaps some chopped celeriac in the boil, a squirt of celery purée in the secondary, dry-hopped with celery seed, would certainly taste of celery. Whether it would taste nice is another matter – do feel free to try it.

But what vegetables lack (by and large) in the flavour department they make up for to a surprising extent in convertible starches and available sugar. The best place for them, then, is surely the mash tun, where plentiful amylase will coax it all out of them. A word of warning, though: soggy vegetable pulp is almost bound to stick your mash utterly and completely, so either steep your veg in a mesh bag or use plenty of rice hulls. Or do both. Anyway, if your fancy is tickled, below is a short list, each with the sketchiest imaginable detail, of a mere handful of vegetables (and two fruits) that brewers have used successfully. There may well be many, many more – and unless craft brewers somehow lose their curiosity, there certainly will be one day!

> **Banana:** the pulped flesh of the banana can be added to the secondary like any other tropical fruit (see 'Other Flavourings', below), and will actually be more assertive and flavoursome than most of them. But the truly inquisitive brewer will want to try recreating the genuine banana beer of so many East African countries, in which the fruit is the diastatic portion of the mash, both carrying a high sugar content of its own and converting the starches in unmalted sorghum. The fruit is used in the form of a thick, sweet juice, which is extracted by mashing the flesh with an equal quantity of lemongrass and hanging the resulting pulp over a bowl in a muslin bag. That, at least, is the theory. The juice is then poured over the bruised sorghum, liquor is added and the sweet wort is pitched without hops. Does this

actually work? Well, it seems to in East Africa but we have no independent confirmation.

Carrot: carrots are quite sweet, containing 10g carbohydrates (of which 4.7-5g is sugar) per 100g of flesh. Ideally they need to be converted in the mashtun, but alternatively they can be chopped up and added to the boil or reduced to a purée or even juiced and added to the primary; the later the addition the more strongly the carrot's earthy, spicy flavour comes through. (Remember, though, that juice contains 8g of sugar per 100g.) Several microbrewers in the US and Australia are now making carrot beers; the most popular foundation seems to be a saison, which given that saisons were originally fairly rough-and-ready farm beers seems highly appropriate.

Chicory root: the bitterness for which Cichorium intybus is prized arises from the two anti-parasitic and insecticidal lactones, lactucin and lactucopicrin, which are mostly concentrated in the root and are also partly responsible for chicory's intense woody and earthy flavours. It has a long tradition of use as an adjunct in Flemish and Dutch beers such as witloofbier, a wheat beer in which chicory root replaces some of the bittering hops. Despite its bitterness, though, chicory root is among the most sugary of vegetables, containing 11g of digestible carbohydrate of which 8.5-9g is sugar per 100g. The leaves are blander and have little to offer the brewer: keep them for salad.

Garden peas: when one thinks of malt one always thinks of cereals, but soaking and kilning legumes produces the same result, and malted peas have been used in mash tuns in many parts of the world for centuries. Sometimes they're used to pad out scarce malted barley, as in Soviet-era Lithuania. Sometimes they're used to pad out heavily taxed malted barley, as in Britain during World War I and, indeed, in modern Japan. And as fermentable material, cheapness is indeed their chief virtue: they contain 6.8g of carbohydrates, of which 4g is sugar, per 100g, and they clog the outflow of the mash tun and can turn a 20-minute run-off into a five-hour ordeal. However, used at a rate of 5-15 per cent in the mash tun, with rice hulls, they seem to be a valuable aid to fermentation. This is probably because they are nitrogen fixers – replenishing tired soil with nitrogen being their role in crop rotation– and are therefore high in yeast nutrients.

Kelp: *see* Seaweed.

Marrow aka Squash: *see* Pumpkin.

Nettles: nothing gives depth and fullness to a very light-bodied beer like a major addition of newly shot tops of peppery, nutrient-rich Urtica dioica. You definitely need rubber gloves, and a fair bit of determination, to get out and about in April collecting enough fresh nettle-tops for nettle beer. You need a kilo – that's a well-stuffed carrier bag – to make a five-litre brew, so if you really wanted to make a commercial quantity you (and most of your family) would be picking for quite a few days. Unfortunately nettles aren't to everyone's taste – they're rather earthy and need the juice of two whole lemons to liven up a 5-litre brew. They're also not terribly high in carbohydrates at 7g per 100g, but they're incredibly rich in minerals and vitamins, most of which will survive the boil unscathed and will go on to keep your yeast fed and active.

M
A
S
H
E
D

V
E
G
E
T
A
B
L
E
S

Parsnip: one of the home winemaker's favourite ingredients both for its high carbohydrate level (18g per 100g including 4.8g sugar) and for its distinctive flavours. Thanks to the root's high concentration of terpinolene, which makes up 40-70 per cent of its essential oil, and myristicin, the parsnip's aromatics are very pungently smoky and spicy but with darker, earthier underlying notes of wood, nuts and liquorice. Winemakers either have to gelatinise the parsnip's starches by boiling, or have to add amylase; this isn't necessary for the brewer whose mash will be swimming with the malt's own surplus enzyme. Choose roots whose sugars have been concentrated by one or two frosts (although the cores of parsnips that have been left in the ground too long turn woody), and leave them somewhere warm and dry for a while before use to sweat out some of their 80 per cent moisture content. Then simply slice or chop the flesh – but without peeling, because the surface is where all that terpinolene and myristicin are concentrated – and add to the mash. If you find you really like the flavours (and winemakers compare a well-made parsnip wine to sherry or Madeira), make further additions to the primary and/or secondary fermentations as you go along. Other roots are also suitable for brewing, although perhaps less so than the parsnip: sugar beet has 10g of carbohydrate, of which 7g is sugar, to 100g of flesh; swedes have 9g and 4.5g; perhaps turnips, with 6.8g and 3.4g, belong more to the roasting tin than the mash tun.

Potato: padding out malt with potato starch was common among brewers on both sides of the Atlantic during World War II not so much because there was a shortage of barley, but because there was a shortage of ships and trains to move it about. Potato was a particularly attractive adjunct because while its carbohydrate content of 18g per 100g – more, if the potatoes were part-dried – was considerably greater than that of malt, its use didn't drastically affect the quality of the beer (or at any rate, no more than consumers expected in wartime: fussier modern tasters say potato starch confers an earthy flavour with hints of slug). However it tended to turn into wallpaper paste in the mash and clog up the pipes; and, as one British brewer observed, it gave drinkers terrible wind. Today there are plenty of much more satisfactory alternatives, and the only people who brew with potatoes on any scale are vodka distillers.

Prickly pear: the spiny pad or fruit of Opuntia ficus-indica is added – with great care! – by a number of craft breweries in the US south-west to which it is indigenous, either to the primary as a reduction or to the secondary as a purée. (To make the reduction chop, crush, add a little water, simmer to mush in a closed pot and keep squashing, hydrating and simmering from time to time until you have a good quantity of juice, then strain). It's not a very satisfactory brewing fruit – it contains 10g carbohydrate, of which 1g is sugar, to 100g of fruit, which isn't bad, but it's difficult and messy to process and even in quantity it yields only a very subdued watermelon/cucumber/pear flavour that is easily overwhelmed by hops.

Pumpkins: using pumpkins to pad out the malt dates back to early Colonial times in North America, when barley was scarce. With its 7g of carbohydrates per 100g of flesh, pumpkin made an adequate substitute but not a wildly popular one: it fell out of use as soon as the prairies were opened up to agriculture. It was revived by American microbrewers, mainly as a seasonal beer for the autumn, in the 1980s and has since become, for many, an integral part of Hallowe'en and Thanksgiving. Some say the pumpkin confers little in the way of flavour, and it's the pumpkin pie spices – cloves, cinnamon, nutmeg and ginger – that really make the difference. The pumpkin flesh is generally part-cooked before being added either to the mash or the boil.

Seaweed: Seaweeds of various sorts have been part of the maritime poor's diet since the dawn of time – Welsh laverbread and Irish carrageen are current examples, although the crisp deep-fried seaweed on so many Chinese menus is actually shredded cabbage. In recent years the deep flavours and high nutritional value of seaweeds have made them fashionable restaurant fodder, and where foodies lead, craft brewers follow. There are now several craft beers on the market using species like kombu, bladderwrack and dillisk in the mash, generally in such small quantities that they contribute not much more to the flavour than a dark saltiness (although they are quite high in carbohydrate – typically 10g of which 0.6g is sugar to 100g of dry matter). Where they really score, though, is in their very high yields of yeast nutrient, especially nitrogen. Their main historical use has been as a very potent soil improver; they are an equally potent fermentation improver!

Sweet potato: no relation to the potato, Ipomoea batatas is actually a member of the convolvulus family, as you will immediately recognise should you encounter one in flower. A native American, it's also no relation to the African yam, although it often goes by the name. Its suitability for brewing purposes bears no relation to its flavour, which is negligible but is said to be earthy, but rather to its starch content of 20g, of which 4-6g is sugar to 100g of flesh.

THE
MICROBREWERS'
HANDBOOK

By Ted Bruning

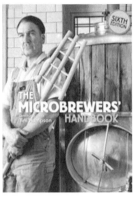

"Indispensable if you are tempted to bolt together mash tun, copper and fermenters"
Roger Protz

"If you are considering creating your own brewery, whatever your motivation, you should buy and read this book as your first step"
Hopmaltbrew.com

The microbrewing scene has changed beyond recognition in the eight years since the first edition of this book was published. The sheer number of small independent breweries at work, up and down the land, has now more than doubled to around 1,500.

Ted Bruning, leading beer author, guides you through the practicalities of starting your own microbrewery; from how to brew right through to finding a place of your own.

- How to source the correct equipment
- Advice on developing the necessary skills, raising the finance and finding appropriate premises
- Specialist advice on the design, promotion and marketing of your beer
- Detailed case studies of those who have started their own microbreweries with the pitfalls explained
- Directory of services and suppliers
- **£12.95 plus postage and packing**

www.posthousepublishing.com

Gluten-free Ingredients

A number of food plants mimic cereals closely enough to produce beer-like alcoholic beverages – or fairly beer-like alcohol beverages, at any rate – that sufferers from coeliac disease and other conditions stemming from gluten intolerance can safely enjoy.

Chief among these is sorghum, a member of the millet family and one of the most important food crops on the planet: not only is it highly nutritious, but it will positively thrive in hot, dry conditions and poor soil where few other food plants can even survive. It has long been used to make a refreshingly sour artisan beer in most of Africa since it undergoes a lactic fermentation as well as an alcoholic one; its use in brewing in Britain and the US dates to World War II, when it was used to pad out inadequate allocations of barley. It is now widely used in commercial brewing in Africa to cut back on the use of expensive imported barley.

An advantage for the brewer is that sorghum is very rich in protein and nitrogen, making for a rapid and efficient fermentation and good foaming and head retention. Its disadvantage is that its grains are so small that it's very difficult to malt, and it makes a horrible sticky mess in the malting that is very difficult to get rid of.

Millet, broadly speaking, is to Asia as sorghum is to Africa: a hardy, nutritious and versatile grain with a long history of use in brewing and, in Nepal, distilling – indeed you might with justice describe rakshi as millet gin. Millet beer is an ancient drink in Taiwan, but it's also found outside Asia: in East Africa it's famously drunk warm and through a straw, while in the South-eastern Balkans it's called 'bozu'.

Another common base for gluten-free beer is buckwheat, the dried and ground seeds of Fagopyrum esculentum, a 'pseudocereal' related to sorrel and rhubarb. This highly nutritious plant is packed with available starches and proteins and is much favoured as an alternative to cereal flour in Brittany where under the name blé noir it is widely used to make pancakes and where it is also distilled to make a spirit sold as whisky.

Very starchy roots, especially the sweet potato (see above), certainly carry a sufficient load of carbohydrates to make a potentially very alcoholic mash, but one perhaps more suited to the still than the hop-kettle. They have very little flavour or aroma of their own, and without adjuncts they make only very light pale ales and lagers that require plenty of help from hops.

And that's the problem with sorghum, millet, buckwheat and other gluten-free alternatives – including that trendiest of pseudocereals, quinoa. They're not cereals, and a pedant would say that the beverage they produce is ipso facto not beer (or whisky). A beer-lover might agree. Nevertheless, a huge amount of research and development has gone into producing palatable gluten-free alternatives to beer, almost all of it funded and conducted by small companies. The lack of a base malt that tastes like malt has always been a problem for them, and most of the available adjuncts and flavourings are as gluten-rich as cereal malt itself, although a syrup derived from brown rice has proved to lend weight if not much flavour to worts of sorghum and buckwheat.

There is and always has been, however, one genuine cereal – not an alternative or a substitute, but a cereal – that is naturally gluten-free: oats. The principal protein in oats, avenin, is sufficiently different from gliadin (the offending constituent of gluten) not to trigger a reaction or, in the case of coeliac sufferers, cause organic damage. Oats have a long history in brewing and are primarily used either malted or unmalted to improve and smooth out the mouthfeel mainly of stouts. Only one maltster – Thomas Fawcett & Sons of Yorkshire, England – regularly makes oat malt, and brewing an all-malt beer would not be straightforward. There is also an ever-present risk of contamination by other grains present in the maltings, although by the time the grist has been liquored down the amount of gluten from contaminants should be below harmful levels.

To study how oat malt can best be used, read *Brewing With 100 per cent Oat Malt, Klose, Mauch et al, Journal of the Institute of Brewing 2011 vol. 117(3) pp.411–421*, available as a PDF at Wiley Online Library.

Liquor and its Treatment

Beer being almost all water (or liquor – in a brewery you wash with water and brew with liquor, and don't you ever forget it!), brewers need to take H2O very seriously indeed.

Traditionally, pretty much all beer used to be brewed with water from the brewery's own well, each with its own mineral profile; many established breweries still use their original wells, and some newer ones have bored their own. The mineral content depends on the rock through which the rainwater that fills the wells has percolated. Where the rock is mainly hard, impervious granite or slate the water takes up almost no minerals, and is (of course) called soft. In districts of soft sedimentary rock – limestone or sandstone – the water dissolves and collects various minerals as it passes through, and is therefore called hard. The minerals of particular interest to the brewer are chalk (calcium carbonate, or calcium bicarbonate in dissolved form) and gypsum (calcium sulphate). One of them you want; one of them you don't.

Chalk and gypsum don't confer a flavour as such, but they do affect the behaviour of the liquor during brewing, which can be critical to the final character of the beer. For what goes on in the mash tun is a lot more complicated than merely dissolving the sugar present in the malt as you might dissolve sugar in your coffee. There are a lot of enzymes in there too, and the minerals can either help or hinder them at every stage – from extraction during the mash through hop extraction during the boil to the performance of the yeast during fermentation. They also contribute significantly to the acidity or pH value of the liquor. It should be mildly acid – a pH of 5.3 is ideal; 5.2 or 5.4 will do; 5.1 or 5.5 are too extreme.

Chalk is the mineral you don't want. Left untreated it breaks down during the boil and deposits limescale, which can damage your heating elements and fur up your pipes. It also increases the acidity of the mash, thus reducing its efficiency; it accentuates the harsher characteristics of the hops, reducing the amount you can use; and its ions even interfere with fermentation.

The one you want, then, is gypsum. It isn't broken down by boiling, so it won't damage your brewing equipment. It reduces mash acidity, enhancing extraction. It mellows the astringency of the hops somewhat, allowing you to make the most of their aromatic properties. It even enhances the clarity of the beer. The well water of Burton upon Trent is especially rich in gypsum, which is one reason why Burton became the birthplace of pale ales; and in fact the process of water treatment is universally known as 'Burtonisation'.

You will be brewing with tap water, almost certainly; and whether you're in a hard or soft water area you will want to treat your liquor before brewing with it. If you're in a hard water area, give your liquor a good boil with a pinch of gypsum for half-an-hour or so the day before you want to use it. The chalk will settle out during the boil, and when it has cooled, simply run it off into a suitable vessel. Give your boiler a good rinse to get rid of the sediment, and then return the clear liquor to the boiler ready for mashing. Also at this stage test the water's acidity with litmus paper: if it's above 5.3 add gypsum in little doses until the required pH is reached. If you're in a soft water area there will be no need for a preliminary boil as there will be no chalk to precipitate. In fact you might even have to add some calcium carbonate (precipitated chalk) to the malt grist before mashing to get the pH down to the right level.

The last stage in your liquor treatment programme comes before you start your mash. Bring your water up to the boil again, add 10 grams of gypsum per 30L of liquor to counteract the decrease in pH that occurs when the malt hits the liquor, and let it bubble for half an hour. Let it cool to mashing temperature, and you're off.

PART TWO

Boil...

ADVERTORIAL

Charles Faram goes for the nose with new UK hop varieties

In 2006 Charles Faram teamed up with world-renowned hop expert Peter Glendinning and local UK hop growers in founding the Charles Faram Hop Development Programme. The shared ambition has been to develop new varieties that follow these core objectives:

- Economically sound varieties with a natural resistance to disease and heavy yield potential
- Disease resistant hedgerow varieties with similar characteristics to traditional hops such as Fuggles and Goldings.
- Interesting new aromas profiles with higher levels of intensity and complex flavours.

More recently the programme has also been extended to work with growers in the USA, Slovenia and the Czech Republic. The programme in the UK has been very successful and has produced a range of popular new varieties that follow this essential brief, such as the following:

Jester: First planted in 2009, Jester was everything you wouldn't expect of a British hop variety, revealing intense aromas of grapefruit, lychee, and berry fruits. Having been cross bred between an agronomically strong British male seedling and the classic US variety Cascade, the early trial samples instantly stood out with its unique characteristics. Jester also proved to be a favourite amongst the hop growers, showing excellent yield potential and disease resistance. Perhaps what is most alluring about Jester is its capability of providing a unique blend of 'new world' style fruit-iness and delicate, British style drinkability. Presenting itself as a distinctive hybrid variety, Jester sits nicely between traditional British varieties and the intense dank aroma hops of the US and NZ. With typical alpha content of around 9-11%, it can be used in a single hop beer but also performs particularly well when blended with other varieties, offering fine compli-mentary flavours. The acreage has increased significantly in recent years and the greater availability of this outstanding hop variety is sure to be an exciting prospect for brewers in search of distinctive new flavours from the British hop range.

Olicana: Another exciting UK variety. Olicana follows the path carved by Jester, with a punchy aroma profile of mango, grapefruit, and passionfruit. Originally planted in 2009, Olicana is a sister of Jester having also been crossed with the US Cascade variety. It shares many of its sibling's positive agronomical attributes such as strong cone integrity and heavy yield potential. However while Jester provides a distinct dank complexity, Olicana offers a cleaner, pure fruit quality, that has led to it obtaining cult status amongst brewers in the UK. Olicana is an exciting new British aroma hop with unique attributes, blending a delicate session-able quality with highly desirable tropical flavours akin to the New World varieties.

Minstrel and Archer: Planted in 2006, Minstrel and Archer were the first hops to come through the breeding programme as named varieties. Both seedlings of Sovereign and hedgerow varieties, these hops have helped to reinforce the available options for classic British hop flavour while also offering refreshing variations on traditional aroma profiles. As aroma hops, Minstrel allures with subtle tangerine citrus and spiced berries, whilst Archer suggests a delicate complexity of Lime, Apricot and Peach.

The Development Programme has proved to be a great asset to the UK hop industry and continues to contribute towards a sustainable and inspiring future for British hops. The search for exceptional new aroma continues both in the UK and further afield with approximately 80,000 seeds produced every year, all with the potential of being the next great hop. There are a number of trial varieties in the system that possess incredible aromas and tons of potential. It's an exciting time for hops worldwide and as the programme continues to evolve, the best could be yet to come.

We have sites in the UK, USA and Canada as well as global distributors that will be pleased to help you with any advice or queries. To contact us visit our website

www.wellhopped.com

1: Hops

It all started, as did so many good things, with the late Bert Grant. Well, that's an exaggeration, but not a huge one. When he opened Grant's Brewpub in Yakima, Washington, in 1982 the microbrewing revolution was already 14 years old, so he was hardly in the vanguard; but what he did pioneer was an almost complete change in how American and British drinkers preferred their beer.

BB (Before Bert), the tannins and bittering acids had been the more prized component of the hop because of their preservative qualities. The aromas and flavours of its oils had not been reckoned so important, with much of the character of the beer – of ale, in particular – coming from its blend of malts. Bert, though, liked his hops and started turning out beers – especially his IPA – whose fruits, flowers, herbs and spices attracted new drinkers, made converts of old ones and inspired newcomers all around the brewing world.

The new emphasis on aroma varieties changed the way hop growers worked, too. Until now, their main concerns had been agronomic and institutes and colleges such as Hüll in Germany, IUNG in Poland, Zatec in the Czech Republic, Wye College in England (tragically closed in 2009) and a whole host in the Pacific Northwest of the US bred new varieties that cropped more heavily and more reliably; whose cones were even more packed with acids than the previous generation; that were easier to harvest; and, crucially, that were more resistant to the many ills that the hop (being in the main asexually reproduced) is heir to. But the growers were not primarily interested in experimenting with oil compositions or alpha-beta ratios: they wanted new varieties that did the same as the old, only better. And when a hop grower stumbled across a new variant that showed some promise – as frequently happened – it was its agronomic strengths that determined whether it would be selected for breeding.

After Bert, breeders and growers started looking to develop different varieties that weren't 'same-but-better' – they wanted something that really was different: that tasted of ginger and geraniums, with wild bouquets of lime and grapefruit and dark undertones of rum and raisin and wafts of resin and roses. The first of the hop-addicted microbrewers wanted flavours and aromas that would differentiate them from the brown twig brewers of yore; then they wanted flavours and aromas that would differentiate them from each other. Now the rising generation – that's you, that is – wants flavours and aromas that will cast you utterly adrift from the safe anchorages of the past and propel you into new, unexplored oceans of myrcene, farnesene, geraniol and pinene. And breeders, an increasing number of whom are straightforward commercial outfits rather than institutes and research stations with access to public funds, are duly obliging you with a glorious, anarchic riot of innovation. There are now around 300 varieties of hop on the market for you to play with, and new ones are being released all the time. Some of them are easily available; others you might have to track down. Some of them are brand new and fire off rainbows of flavours when you rip open the pack; some are old and faint and earthy but will be just the job the next time retro comes around. Others are almost ghosts, living on only in plant collections or in the wild, like the astonishingly low-alpha native hops of Lithuania, and awaiting only the kiss of some prince of craft brewing to awake them from their long sleep.

Wonderful as all this undoubtedly is, it might leave you feeling like a kid allowed to spend a night in a branch of Toys 'R' Us: a catalogue of some sort would help. So here it is.

It is as up-to-date a catalogue as possible, given the pace of change in such a dynamic arena. Between our going to press and your receiving this book several new varieties will have been added to the 300 listed here. Dynamic companies like America's Hop Breeding Company and, in England, Charles Faram of Worcester seem to eject plumes of experimental varieties like an Icelandic geyser blows hot water and steam; in Germany's Hallertau region alone 200 new varieties are currently on trial. Keeping up is all part of the excitement.

But that's not the only challenge we have faced in our research. It used to be that a new variety would take a decade or more from selection to release, and by the time it reached the market its every property had been thoroughly investigated and documented. This is no longer necessarily the case. Not all new varieties take the stage brandishing a complete dossier of analytical data, and discovering the precise percentages of acids and oils utterly defeats the most assiduous of researchers, let alone the potential customer. There are also a number of native varieties from less well-marshalled jurisdictions that have never even been analysed. But the great majority of entries, we hope, are detailed enough to be of service to the brewer even if some varieties listed will, inevitably, have little more to their names than their names.

If collecting all the data has been a challenge, deciding how to organise it in the most user-friendly manner has been even more so; and having debated all the options we have settled on the ostensibly least useful of all: by country of origin. It would have been an impressive feat to have arranged our entries by some severely practical criterion such as, say, alpha acid content, but every cone is such a damned little Pandora's Box of biochemical components that to organise by a continuum of one of them would only have been to disorganise by a discontinuum of all the others. At least a listing by country of origin gives the brewer some clue as to what is likeliest to be available.

Our final challenge was to decide how much analytical data to include in each entry. Our decision rested on a balance of three factors: utility, length of entry and availability of data. In ideal cases each entry will include the variety's name; its purpose; its parentage and, briefly, its history; an idea of its character; its alpha-beta acid profile; total oils in millilitres per 100g dry weight; the ratios of the more significant oils; and finally a few suggested substitutions. Taken together this should, we hope, be enough to tell the reasonably experienced home or craft brewer what to expect from an unfamiliar variety.

Australia

Cluster (Aus): dual-use hop of mixed Dutch, English and US ancestry.
Character: strongly resinous, herbal.
Alpha 5.5-8.5%, beta 4.5-5.5%, cohumulone 36-42%.
Total oil 0.4-1ml. Myrcene 45-55%, humulene 15-18%, caryophyllene 6-7%, farnesene <1%.
Substitutes: Northern Brewer, Galena.

Ella: high-alpha variety released 2007. Half-sister to Galaxy and the offspring of Spalt and a tetraploid female. Formerly called Stella.
Character: in modest amounts noble with floral notes. Larger dosages are fruity with a hint of aniseed.
Alpha 13.3-16.3%, beta 4.8-7.8%, cohumulone 34-38%.
Total oil 2.4-3.4ml. Myrcene 40-50%, humulene 16-22%, caryophyllene 12-18%, farnesene <1%.

Feux-Coeur Français: bittering hop with genetic roots in Burgundy. Bred to suit the climate of the southern state of Victoria; released 2010. Rare outside Australia.
Alpha 12-16%, beta 3.1%-6%.

Flinders: New high-alpha hybrid privately bred in Western Australia, said to be similar to Columbus. One of many new varieties coming from hop farms in the state, where the supply of distinctive native varieties from individual growers is having a hard time keeping up with demand from the burgeoning craft brewing sector.
Alpha 11%.

Galaxy: high-alpha dual-purpose triploid descended from Perle and released in 2009, Galaxy has the world's highest

percentage of oils and as a result its popularity has spread far beyond its native shores.
Character: intense citrus, peach and passion fruit aromas.
Alpha 11-16%, beta 5-6.9%, cohumulone 32-42%.
Total oil 3-5ml. Myrcene 33-69, humulene 1-2%, caryophyllene 7-9%, farnesene 2-4%.
Substitutes: Citra, Amarillo, Centennial.

Helga aka Southern Hallertau: another member of the Hallertau family, Helga is a versatile aroma variety bred in 1996. Production is increasing as craft brewers begin to take interest.
Character: noble, mildly floral and spicy.
Alpha 5.4-7.3%, beta 5-7%, cohumulone 20-23%.
Total oil 0.6-1ml. Myrcene 1-13%, humulene 35-55%.
Caryophyllene 10-15%.
Substitutes: Hallertauer Mittelfrüh.

Kracanup: like Flinders and Red Earth, a privately developed hybrid from Western Australia. A cross between Cascade and Chinook, named after the farm on which it was bred and not, apparently, as an Ozzie joke.
Alpha 5%.
Total oil 1.5ml.

Melba: the 'Dame of Hops' as it's known, is a dual-purpose variety with high oil content from Willersie Hops. Released in 2004, it only took off in 2015 when Cooper's chose it for that year's vintage ale, so details are still somewhat sketchy. Best as a late hop.
Character: clean spicy bitterness, aromas of summer fruits (passion fruit, stonefruit) and sharp grapefruit citrus.
Alpha 7-10%, beta 2.5-5%, cohumulone 25-35%.

Total oil 2-4ml.
Substitutes: Galaxy.

Pride of Ringwood: revered bittering hop developed in the 1950s by Carlton & United Breweries from Pride of Kent at its research station at Ringwood, Victoria, and used in all its beers for many decades. At one point in its history Pride of Ringwood accounted for 90 per cent of Australia's hop acreage. Not a great traveller, though: it crops too late for most growers in the Northern Hemisphere. Can be used as a late addition, although many brewers say it disappoints and prefer to twin it with a suitable aroma variety.
Character: spicy, fruity, earthy aromas.
Alpha 7-11%, beta 4-8%, cohumulone 33-39%.
Total oil 1-2ml. Myrcene 25-53%, humulene 2-8%, caryophyllene 5-10%, farnesene 1%.
Substitutes: Pacific Gem, Cluster, Northern Brewer.

Red Earth: independently bred new aroma variety from Western Australia. A cross between Columbus and a Goldings-derived male, named for the reddish colour of the new cones. Released 2012.
Character: earthy, spicy, woody aroma and flavour with a note of citrus.
Alpha 9%.

Stella: *see* Ella.

Summer aka Australian Summer: low-alpha aroma variety bred from Saaz by Hop Products Australia; released 1997. A great dry hop, not as spicy as its Czech parent but lusciously aromatic.
Character: gentle but distinctive flavours and aromas of

apricot, melon, peach and grass.
Alpha 5.6-6.4%, beta 4.8-6.1%, cohumulone 20-25%.
Total oil 1.4-2ml. Myrcene 29-38%, humulene 28-50%,
caryophyllene 8-11%, farnesene <1%.
Substitutes: Saaz.

Super Pride: high-alpha version of Pride of Ringwood, bred
in 1987 by Hop Products Australia at Rostrevor Breeding
Garden, Victoria, released 1995. Now Australia's leading
bittering hop, but with some mild aroma.
Character: resin, spice and citrus.
Alpha 13.5-15%, beta 6.4-6.9%, cohumulone 26.8-28%.
Total oil 2.1-2.6ml. Myrcene 19-34%, humulene 1-2%,
caryophyllene 5-8%, farnesene <1%.
Substitutes: Pride of Ringwood.

Sylva: aroma hop bred from Saaz in Tasmania in 1997, with
a subtle and complex flavour profile suited to light lagers.
Astronomical farnesene content lends itself perfectly to
dry-hopping.
Character: herbal and earthy aromas. A resinous flavour
that has been compared to freshly cut timber.
Alpha 5.6-7.3%, beta 3-4.6%, cohumulone 20-25%.
Total oils 1-1.4ml. Myrcene 26-36%, humulene 18%-27%,
caryophyllene 5-8%, farnesene 22-28%.
Substitutes: Hallertau Mittlefrüh, Helga, Saaz.

Topaz: high-alpha cross of English and Australian varieties
launched 1985, originally as a bittering hop but recently
rediscovered as a late addition capable of creating truly
intense aromas, especially when combined with citrus-rich
partners such as Galaxy in higher-gravity beers.
Character: light tropical fruit flavours, including lychee,

clove-like spice, earth, resin and grass when used to dry-hop.

Alpha 13.7-17.7%, beta 6.4-7.9%, cohumulone 48-51%.

Total oil 1.7-2.2ml. Myrcene 34-56%, humulene 8-13%, caryophyllene 7-13%, farnesene <1%.

Substitutes: Galaxy, Citra, Cascade, Riwaka, Rakau, Amarillo.

Vic Secret aka Victoria's Secret: sister of Topaz, released 2013. Dual-purpose hop that performs best in the whirlpool or via dry-hopping. Late kettle additions create a distinct earthiness, but at the expense of fruitiness.

Character: tropical fruit especially passion fruit and pineapple, pine, herbs.

Alpha 14-17%, beta 6.1-7.8%, cohumulone 51-56%.

Total oils 2.2–2.8ml. Myrcene 38-41%, humulene 12-21%, caryophyllene 11-15%, farnesene <1%.

Substitutes: Galaxy.

Belgium

Blue Northern Brewer: natural mutant with deep reddish-blue leaves found in a Belgian hop yard and released as an ornamental variety in 1992. Makes a passable dual-purpose brewing hop.

Alpha 6-8%, beta 3-4%, cohumulone 24%.

Total oil 0.76ml. Myrcene 27-40%, humulene 29%, caryophyllene 10%.

Coigneau: historic Belgian variety first cultivated in the Aalst-Asse hop yards in the 18th century. Prized for its high yield and wilt-resistance and favoured for use in lambics because of its low alpha content, it became the country's dominant hop in the 19th century and was also used for hopping Pilsners. After 1930 it was replaced by more modern varieties and the last commercially grown bines were finally grubbed up in 1950. However, Coigneau is still grown in small quantities at Poperinghe and used by the Cantillon lambic brewery, and plans are in hand in England to revive this most authentic of Belgian hops.

Groene Bel: authentic and old-established aroma variety probably selected from native Aalst hops in the late 19th or early 20th century. All but vanished after World War II when it was replaced by Saaz and Hallertau. Although it is no longer commercially produced, it has been used for breeding purposes in Slovenia. Note its high humulene content.
Character: earthy continental aroma.
Alpha 4.9%, beta 3.5%, cohumulone 27%.
Total oil 0.98ml. Myrcene 39%, humulene 32%, caryophyllene 18%, farnesene 2.41%.

Nordgaard: obsolete aroma variety distantly descended from Spalter. Still used for breeding, particularly in Slovenia.
Alpha 7.5%, beta 3.4%, cohumulone 29%.
Total oil 0.94ml. Myrcene 47%, humulene 27%, caryophyllene 11%, farnesene 1.7%.

Record: aroma hop bred in the 1960s from Saaz and Northern Brewer, which it strongly resembles. Also grown in Germany.
Character: European aroma, mildly fruity.
Alpha 7-12%, beta 4-8%, cohumulone 27%.
Total oil 1.82ml. Myrcene 50%, humulene 24-28%, caryophyllene 8.2%, farnesene 0.16%.

Substitutes: Northern Brewer.

Star: old aroma variety largely discontinued due to poor vigour and yield but still obtainable in small quantities for home brewing.

Alpha 3.2%, beta 1.7%, cohumulone 24%.

Total oil 0.47ml. Myrcene 34.2%, humulene 33.9%, caryophyllene 11.7%, farnesene 3.7%.

China

Kirin Flower: aromatic variety originating from the hop-breeding programme at Japan's Kirin brewery.

Marco Polo: aroma variety.
Alpha 12%; beta 3%.

SA-1: bittering hop.
Alpha 2-4%; beta 2-5%.
Farneses 11-15%.

Tsingtao Flower: dual-purpose variety bred from Cluster. Makes up 90 per cent of China's hop production.

Character: floral, earthy, woody and spicy flavours. Very complex aromas: tobacco, green tea, jasmine, blackcurrant, grapefruit, orange and clove.

Alpha 6-8%; beta 3-4.2%.

Total oil 0.4-0.6mg. Myrcene 45-55%; humulene 15-18%.

Substitutes: Galena, Magnum.

Czech Republic

Agnus: high-alpha hop released in 2001. Although primarily a bittering hop, its oil content makes it eminently suitable for single-varietal use.

Character: strong spicy citrus and herbal notes; grassy

aroma with a hint of lychee.
Alpha 9-15%, beta 4-6.5%, cohumulone 30-40%.
Total oil 2-3ml. Myrcene 40-55%, humulene 15-20%, caryophyllene 4.3%.

Amethyst: aroma variety not well known outside its native land, but thanks to its low alpha content it can be a characterful addition to more full-bodied beers.
Character: rich, woody, earthy flavours; citrus and spicy aroma.
Alpha 2-6%, beta 7-8%, cohumulone 20-28%.
Total oil 0.4-1ml. Myrcene 42%, humulene 19%, caryophyllene 6%.
Substitute: Saaz.

Blato: aroma variety; a regional red-bine member of the Saaz family. One of eight clones of old-established Czech varieties released in 1978 with varying degrees of success: the others were Aromat, Lucan, Osvald clones 31, 72 and 114, Sirem and Zlatan.
Character: delicate noble aroma.
Alpha 4.5%, beta 3.5%, cohumulone 21%.
Total oil 0.65mg. Myrcene 47%, humulene 18%, caryophyllene 5%, farnesene 11.2%.

Bohemie: heavy-cropping and wilt-resistant Saaz-Sladek cross from Zatec; released 2010.
Character: herbs dominate, with floral and spicy notes.
Alpha 3-8%, beta 6-9%, cohumulone 23-26%.
Total oil 1-1.5ml. Myrcene 30-45%, humulene 17-23%, caryophyllene 7-10%, farnesene 1-3%.

BOR: aroma hop; either a seedling of Hallertauer Mittel-früeh or a hybrid of Saaz and Northern Brewer. Low alpha content has held it back commercially.
Character: slightly spicy;very like Saaz.
Alpha 2-3%, beta 3-4%, cohumulone 14-20%.
Total oil 0.65ml. Myrcene 21%, humulene 46%, caryophyllene 13%.

Harmonie: aroma variety bred from Saaz, registered 2004. Agronomics and brewing potential are said to be sound, but acreage is so far limited.
Character: noble, slightly spicy.
Alpha 5-8%, beta 5-8%, cohumulone 19-22%.
Total oil 0.9-1.4ml. Myrcene 30-40%, Humulene 10-20%, caryophyllene 6-11%, farnesene <1%.
Substitutes: Saaz.

Kazbek: aroma variety bred from Saaz and wild hops from the Caucasus Mountains, released 2008. Ideal for lagers and Belgian-style ales.
Character: spicy like Saaz, earthy and with a hint of lemon.
Alpha 5-8%, beta4.6%, cohumulone 35-40%.
Total oil 0.9-1.8ml. Myrcene 40-55%, humulene 2-35%, caryophyllene 10-15%, selinene 1-3%.
Substitutes: Saaz.

Rubin: bittering variety bred from Saaz, Northern Brewer and Bor, registered 2007.
Character: spicier than Saaz.
Alpha 9-12%, beta 3.5-5%, cohumulone 25-35%.
Total oil 1-2ml. Myrcene 30-45%, humulene 15-25%, caryophyllene 7-10%, farnesene <1%.
Substitutes: Agnus.

H
O
P
S

Saaz: one of the four noble hops alongside Tettnanger, Hallertauer and Spalt and possibly the oldest variety still growing with a pedigree of seven centuries or thereabouts. A truly promiscuous breeder too. Originating in Zatec, Bohemia (now in the Czech Republic), it is grown around the world and is the progenitor of countless other varieties. New Zealand in particular has taken Saaz to its heart, breeding descendants including Motueka and Riwaka (B & D Saaz, respectively). A low alpha content and high farnesene make Saaz a gentle aroma hop that gives a delicate bittering when added early.
Character: herbal, earthy, cinnamon-spicy.
Alpha 2.5-4.5%, beta 4-6%, cohumulone 23-26%.
Total oil 0.4-0.8ml. Myrcene 25-40%, humulene 15-30%, caryophyllene 6-9%, farnesene 14-20%.
Substitutes: Saaz (US), Sterling, Lublin, Motueka, Centennial, Amarillo, Tettnanger, Ultra, Crystal.

Sladek: aroma hop released 1994; cross between Saaz and Northern Brewer.
Character: aroma and flavours of peach and passion fruit.
Alpha 4.5-8%, beta 4-7%, cohumulone 23-30%.
Total oil 1.0-2m. Myrcene 35-50%, humulene 20-40%, caryophyllene 9-14%, farnesene <1%.
Substitutes: Saaz.

Universal: Czech dual-purpose hop delisted as a commercial variety before 1991 owing to poor vigour and low yield. It is still grown in the US and remains a firm favourite with craft and home brewers, especially in lighter beers.
Character: earthy, spicy and floral noble aromas and mild bitterness.
Alpha 5.2%, beta 3.7%, cohumulone 23%.

Substitutes: Hallertauer Mittelfrüh.

Vital: dual-purpose hop from the Zatec Breeding Programme, released 2008. Originally bred for pharmaceutical use with high levels of the antioxidant xanthohumol. High alpha and beta create a good balance of bitterness and aroma, making Vital an excellent single-varietal.
Character: spicy and earthy, and its fresh hop aroma balances the bitterness.
Alpha 14-17%, beta 8-11%.
Substitutes: Saaz, Styrian Golding.

England

Admiral: Bittering variety descended from Northdown and Challenger. Released by Wye College in 1998 as a high-alpha successor to Target. A good dry hop.
Character: orange and herbal notes.
Alpha 13-16%, beta 5-6%, cohumulone 37-48%.
Total oil 1-1.7ml. Myrcene 39-48%, humulene 23-26%, caryophyllene 6-7%, farnesene 1.8-2.2%.
Substitutes: Chinook, Northdown, Challenger, Centennial, Cascade, Amarillo, Target.

Alliance: aroma hop bred from Whitbread Golding Variety at Wye College in the 1960s as a possible successor to Fuggle alongside Progress. Not a success, and no longer grown commercially.
Alpha 4.6-7.5%, beta 1.6-5.1%, cohumulone 29%.
Total oil 0.4-1.75ml. Myrcene 36.7%, humulene 33%, farnesene 1.9%.

Archer: aroma and dry-hopping variety developed by Charles Faram Ltd of Worcester, released 2013.

Representative of a new wave of English aroma hops.
Character: floral and fruity with distinctive apricot, lime and peach notes.
Alpha 4-6%, beta 2-3%, cohumulone 32-38%.
Total oils 0.6-0.8ml. Myrcene 20-25%, humulene 26-30%, farnesene 0.4%.

Beata: High-beta bittering hedgerow variety bred by Horticulture Research International at Wye College, Kent, and released 2006.
Character: soft flavours and aromas of honey, apricot and almond.
Alpha 3-6%, beta 9-11%, cohumulone 25-35%.
Total oils 1-1.5ml. Myrcene 28%, humulene 4-8%. **Substitutes:** Belma, Boadicea.

Boadicea: Aphid-resistant dual-purpose hedgerow hop developed by HRI, released 2004.
Character: Delicate aroma of orchard blossoms and grass; subtly spicy.
Alpha 7.5-10%, beta 2.2-4.2%, cohumulone 23-29%.
Total oil 1.4-2.2ml. Myrcene 33%, humulene 20%, caryophyllene 15-19%, farnesene 5%, selinene 5%.

Bramling Cross: old-established dual-purpose hop from Wye College. Result of a Bramling Golding cross with a wild Manitoban hop in the 1920s as an experiment in disease resistance; released 1951. Good bittering qualities in British or British-style ales, but more popular as a fruity late addition especially well suited to rich winter ales and fruit beers. Best used in large quantities.
Character: intensely complex and fruity, with notes of lemon, pear, plum and, most famously, blackcurrant.

Alpha 5-8%, beta 2.3-3.5%, cohumulone 33-35%.
Total oil 0.7-1.2ml. Myrcene 36%, humulene 25%, caryo-
phyllene 14-18%, farnesene <1%.
Substitutes: Whitbread Golding, Progress, East Kent
Golding.

Bramling: popular and prolific aroma hop in 19th-century
England, widely cultivated until its low yield caused it to
fall out of favour. Still grown in British Columbia.
Alpha 5.8%, beta 3%, cohumulone 27%.
Total oil 0.9ml.
Substitutes: Whitbread Golding, Progress, East Kent
Golding.

Brewer's Gold: bittering hop developed at Wye College in
1919; ancestor of modern high-alpha strains including
Sterling, Nugget, Galena, Horizon and Centennial. Both
Brewer's Gold and Bullion are seedlings of BB1, found wild
in Manitoba. Despite its longstanding popularity, it was
rendered commercially redundant by super-alpha bittering
varieties in the 1980s. However, it is grown as breeding
stock and still a good choice for late bittering.
Character: spice and blackcurrant.
Alpha 8-11%, beta 3-6.5%, cohumulone 36-45%.
Total oil 1.96ml. Myrcene 66.7%, humulene 11.6%, caryo-
phyllene 6.5%, farnesene 1%.
Substitutes: Bullion, Cascade, Galena, Northern Brewer
(US), Northdown.

Bullion: bittering variety often used as a late addition.
Sibling of Brewer's Gold but more suited to darker beers.
Bred at Wye College in 1919 from a wild hop cutting from
Manitoba; released 1938. Once popular in professional

H
O
P
S

brewing circles, now superseded by super-alpha varieties with greater bittering potential. Later higher-alpha variants have included Bullion 6 and Bullion 10A.

Character: earth, resin, spice, dark fruits.

Alpha 6.7-12.9%, beta 3.7-9.1%, cohumulone 39%.

Total oil 1.14-2.7ml. Myrcene 45-55%, humulene 23-30%, caryophyllene 9-11%.

Substitutes: Columbus, Northern Brewer, Galena, Chinook, Brewer's Gold.

Challenger aka Wye Challenger: popular dual-purpose hop released in 1972, developed at Wye College from Northern Brewer and and a Hüller variety. Outstandingly successful during the 1980s and 1990s when it was widely planted in both of the UK's hop-growing regions and in Belgium. Good kettle variety; also late and dry hop.

Character: strongly fruity, floral, spice, cedar, green tea.

Alpha 6.5-9%, beta 3.2-4.5%, cohumulone 20-25%.

Total oil 1-1.7ml. Myrcene 30-42%, humulene 25-32%, caryophyllene 8-10%, farnesene 1-3%.

Substitutes: Perle, Northern Brewer, Admiral, East Kent Goldings, Phoenix, Styrian Goldings.

Defender: 1950s Wye College cross between various Goldings and a wild New Mexican hop. Along with its sister variety Density, it was an attempt to create a highly resistant aroma hop just as European winegrowers had overcome phylloxera a century earlier through the use of resistant American rootstock. It failed because of poor yield and low alpha content.

Alpha 4%, beta 1.5%, cohumulone 27%.

Total oil 0.5ml.

Density: shared the same heritage, the same flaws and the same fate as its sibling, Defender.
Alpha 4.4-6.6%, beta 3.3%, cohumulone 36%.
Total oil 0.44. Myrcene 57%, humulene 17%, caryophyllene 7%, farnesene 0.3%.

Early Prolific/EarlyPromise: two of the older examples of Wye College's ceaseless search for wilt-resistant, high-yield aroma hops to succeed the venerable (and vulnerable) Fuggle. These two go back to an almost random mass selection in the 1950s: Early Promise had the higher alpha at 6.1 per cent compared to Early Prolific's 4.7 per cent; Early Prolific had the higher oil content, with good levels of both myrcene and humulene. Neither variety, though, had the yields to make them commercially viable. Another variety that emerged from this exercise but never caught on commercially was Janus.

Endeavour: very characterful dual-purpose hop bred in 2002 at Wye College, released 2015 to an enthusiastic welcome.
Character: aromas and flavours of blackcurrant, logan-berry, spice, grapefruit, lime.
Alpha 8-10.5%, beta 3.8-5.3%, cohumulone 30-36%.
Total oil 1.1-1.7ml. Myrcene 27-37%, farnesene 5-8%, humulene 3-10%.

Epic: found in 1987 on a farm in Kent in a field that had once grown Alliance hops, Epic was regarded as an orna-mental strain until 2004 when its consistently strong crop-ping led to its development mainly as a bittering hop, but also as a good late-addition aromatic.
Character: deep berry-fruit aroma, herbal flavour.

H
O
P
S

Alpha: 3-5%, beta 1.7-2.5%, cohumulone 30-33%.
Total oil 0.4-0.8ml. Myrcene 12%, humulene 42%,
farnesene 1.5%.

Ernest: a real comeback kid of a hop, Ernest was originally
one of the generation of neomexicanus crosses conducted
at Wye in the 1920s, farm-trialled in 1957-8 and brew-
ery-trialled in 1959. It was rejected partly on the grounds
of its 'strong, coarse, American aroma' and survived only
in Wye's plant archive. It has now been resurrected because
a 'strong, coarse, American aroma', arising in part from
notably high levels of geraniol and linalool, is exactly what
today's brewers and drinkers want!
Character: strong apricot, citrus and spice aromas.
Alpha 5.3-6.3%, beta 4.5-5%, cohumulone 50-55%.
Total oil 0.7-1.1%. Myrcene 55%, humulene 10%.

Flyer: dual-purpose hop bred at Wye from a high-alpha
female and a low trellis-type male hop, only recently
released. Ideally suited to dark, full-bodied ales and stouts.
Characterful dry hop.
Character: citrus, resin, stone fruit, liquorice, treacle toffee,
caramel.
Alpha 8.3-14.5%, beta 4.1-6%, cohumulone 26-35%.
Total oil 0.6ml. Myrcene 17.4-25%, humulene 22.5%,
farnesene 0.7%.

First Gold: dual-purpose variety bred from Whitbread
Golding at Wye College, released 1996. England's first
commercial hedgerow hop. An ideal single-varietal, it
combines a solid bittering performance with a very versatile aroma profile. A modern classic and hugely popular.
Character: tangerine, orange, geranium and cinnamon

aromas, marmalade and magnolia flavours.

Alpha 5.6-9.3%, beta 2.3-4.1%, cohumulone 31-36%.

Total oil 0.7-1.5ml. Myrcene 24-28%, humulene 20-24%, caryophyllene 1.3%, farnesene 2-4%.

Substitutes: Willamette, East Kent Golding, Styrian Golding, Crystal.

Fuggle: The classic English aroma hop, known as Styrian Golding in Europe and a parent of many New World hops such as Cascade, Centennial and Willamette. Noticed growing wild in Horsmonden, Kent, in 1861 and sold commercially as a dual-purpose variety until superseded by much higher-alpha modern strains. Tragically vulnerable to wilt, Wye Hops is currently working on a resistant seedling.

Character: minty, grassy, earthy and floral flavours and aromas.

Alpha 3.5-6.5%, beta 2-4%, cohumulone 27-33%.

Total oil 0.7-1.1ml. Myrcene 25-30%, humulene 30-38%, caryophyllene 9-10%, farnesene 6-8%.

Substitutes: Willamette, Fuggle (US), Styrian Golding, Tettnanger, Newport.

Fusion: blend of experimental aroma varieties from Charles Faram.

Character: changes every year, from citrus/spice to tropical fruit.

Alpha 7-9%, cohumulone 23-28%.

Total oil 0.6-1.2%.

Golden Tassles aka Diva: ornamental hedgerow variety released by East Malling Research Institute in 2003. Grows to 2-3m with dense, very pale foliage and a heavy crop of dark bronze cones. Has been found by home brewers to possess moderate bittering qualities and a fresh, herby aroma.

Golding: the oldest-established English hop variety was developed in the 1790s from the Whitebines of Farnham, Mathon and Canterbury and is actually a family of clones that harvest at different times including Cobb's, Amos's Early Bird, Eastwell, Petham and East Kent. Uniquely, the East Kent Golding (which dates back to 1838) enjoys a Protected Designation of Origin. The Golding is mostly used for bittering and late hopping, often in combination with the other half of the classic double-act, Fuggle.
Character: gently floral, spicy, earthy, honeyed flavours and aromas.
Alpha 4-9.5%, beta 1.9-3%, cohumulone 25-30%.
Total oil 0.4-0.8ml. Myrcene 25%, humulene 36%, caryophyllene 13%.

Herald: dual-purpose variety and one of the first of the hedgerow hops introduced by English growers in the mid-1990s. Very popular with craft breweries.
Character: orange and grapefruit aromas
Alpha 11.9-12.8%, beta 4.8-5.5%, cohumulone 35-37%.
Total oil 1-1.9ml. Myrcene 40%, humulene 15%, caryophyllene 7%, farnesene <1%.
Substitutes: Pioneer.

Jester: Newly developed by hop merchant and breeder Charles Faram Ltd of Worcester, Jester is a British aroma variety calculated to mount a bold challenge to the dominance of American strains.
Character: punchy grapefruit, tropical fruits, blackcurrant, herbs.

Alpha 7-9%, beta 4-6%, cohumulone 23-28%.
Total oil 0.6-1.2ml. Myrcene 45-50%, humulene 2%,
farnesene 0.1-0.2%.

Keyworth's Early: like Ernest, a venerable aroma hop bred
in the 1920s from a wilt-resistant New Mexican parent,
discontinued due to low yield. Recently revived by the
Charles Faram Hop Development Programme for its sharp
citrus quality.
Character: lemon and grapefruit notes.
Alpha 8.6%, beta 3.3%, cohumulone 33%.
Total oil 1.39ml. Myrcene 45%, humulene 22%, caryophyllene 7%.
Substitutes: Keyworth's Midseason.

Keyworth's Midseason: like Keyworth's Early and many
other aroma varieties of the time (and evoking memories of the phylloxera plague of the 1860s), an example of
North American stocks being imported for their resistance to wilt. A cross between Fuggle and a wild American
female, Keyworth's Midseason proved more popular than
Keyworth's Early and was planted on nearly 600 acres by
1954. Also now revived by Charles Faram.
Character: citrus and blackcurrant.
Alpha 7.5%, beta 3.1%, cohumulone 46%.
Total oil 0.89ml. Myrcene 56%, humulene 13%, caryophyllene 10%.
Substitutes: Fuggle.

Minstrel: Another distinctive and characterful newcomer from Charles Faram's Hop Development Programme,
Minstrel is an aroma variety that also creates fullness and
depth of flavour thanks to its high farnesene percentage.

Character: spice, berries, herbs, orange.
Alpha 5-7%, beta 3-3.5%, cohumulone 22-26%.
Total oils 0.5-0.7ml. Myrcene 22-25%, humulene 1-4%, farnesene 7-9%.

Northdown: mildew-resistant dual-purpose hop bred at Wye College in the early 1970s from Northern Brewer and Challenger. Particularly good in the early to mid stages of the boil; often chosen for darker beers.
Character: flowery, piney, berries, resin and spice.
Alpha 7-10%, beta 4-5.5%, cohumulone 24-32%.
Total oil 1.2-2.5ml. Myrcene 23-29%, humulene 37-45%, caryophyllene 13-17%, farnesene 0-1%.
Substitutes: Challenger, Admiral, Phoenix.

Northern Brewer: hugely successful dual-use hop developed at Wye College in 1934 and still grown all around the world today, mostly in Germany and the US. Originally a cross between a Canterbury Golding female and a male, OB21. Suited to ale styles from lambic to porter, usually as a mild bittering hop in conjunction with other aroma varieties.
Character: aromas and flavours of fruit, mint, wood, earth, pine and resin.
Alpha 9.5%, beta 4%, cohumulone 26%.
Total oil 1.61ml. Myrcene 56%, humulene 21%, caryophyllene 7.6%, farnesene <1%.
Substitutes: Hallertau, Pride of Ringwood, Bullion.

Olicana: Another new-wave aroma hop from the Charles Faram stable, with luscious fruitiness countered by a hint of sharp citrus.
Character: intense mango and passion fruit; grapefruit.
Alpha 6-9%, beta 4-6%, cohumulone 28-32%.

Total oils 0.5ml. Myrcene 19.5%, humulene 8.6%.

Omega: aroma hop, the last new variety produced by Dr RA Neve before retiring as head of Wye College's Hop Section in 1984. Sadly its poor storage stability, wilt resistance and yield denied it a commercial foothold.
Character: European aroma.
Alpha 9-10%, beta 3-4%, cohumulone 29%.
Total oil 1.72ml. Myrcene 53%, humulene 17%, caryophyllene 5%.

Phoenix: dual-purpose hop from Wye, aseedling of Yeoman released 1996 as a more resistant successor to Challenger. Its high oil content makes Phoenix an interesting choice as a late hop.
Character: aromas of pine, chocolate and molasses; floral and slightly spicy.
Alpha 8.5-13.5%, beta 3.3-5.5%, cohumulone 24-33%.
Total oil 1.2-3ml. Myrcene 24-32%, humulene 25-32%, caryophyllene 8-10%, farnesene 1-1.4%.
Substitutes: Northdown, Challenger, East Kent Golding.

Pilgrim: tall sibling of hedgerow varieties First Gold and Herald from Wye, released 2001. Displays first-rate bittering qualities in addition to intense aroma and flavour profiles: a true all-purpose hop, great in the boil from beginning to end.
Character: rounded bitterness, grassy herbs, berries, pears, lemon, grapefruit and spice.
Alpha 9-13%, beta 4-5%, cohumulone 36-38%.
Total oil 1.8ml. Myrcene 36%, humulene 17%, caryophyllene 7.3%, farnesene 0.3%.
Substitutes: Target, Pioneer, Challenger.

Pilot: high-alpha hedgerow variety bred at Wye and released 2001. Distinctive oil balance and clean bittering qualities.
Character: spicy aromatics of lemon and marmalade.
Alpha 9-13%, beta 3.3-5%, cohumulone 35%.
Total oil 0.8-1.4ml. Myrcene 30-40%, humulene 3-6%, farnesene <1%.

Pioneer: dual-purpose hop giving classic English aroma and mild-tempered bittering despite its very high cohumulonelevels. Bred at Wye College from Omega; a sister to Herald, released 1996.
Character: intense bitter lemon, grapefruit, herbs and cedar.
Alpha 8-10%, beta 3.5-4%, cohumulone 36-40%.
Total oil 1-1.8ml. Myrcene 31-36%, humulene 22-24%, caryophyllene 7-8%, farnesene <1%.
Substitutes: East Kent Golding, Herald.
Pride of Kent: vintage dual-purpose variety from Wye, parent of celebrated Australian variety Pride of Ringwood.
Alpha 8-11%, beta 6-8%, cohumulone 35%.
Total oil 2.32ml. Myrcene 70%, humulene 9%,caryophyllene 3%.
Substitutes: Galena.

Prima Donna: ornamental version of First Gold.

Progress: dual-purpose variety developed at Wye in the 1950s as a substitute for the wilt-prone Fuggle; released 1964. Often paired with various Goldings.
Character: moderate bitterness, sweet flowery flavour, Fuggle-like aromas of grass, mint and earth.
Alpha 6-7.5%, beta 2-3.3%, cohumulone 33%.

Total oil 0.8-1ml. Myrcene 29%, humulene 36-42%, caryo-phyllene 10.6-14%.
Substitutes: East Kent Golding, Fuggle.

Saxon aka Wye Saxon: aroma hop bred at Wye College from Svaloef, an obsolete Swedish variety; sister to Viking. A good brewing hop but no longer grown for commercial use. It is instead used predominantly for breeding.
Character: fruity, earthy, herbal aromas.
Alpha 8-10%, beta 4-5%, cohumulone 20%.
Total oil 0.95ml. Myrcene 54%, humulene 11.8%, caryo-phyllene 5.6%, farnesene 6.7%.

Sovereign: dual-purpose hop developed at Wye from Pioneer in the 1990s; released 2006. Rounded and balanced enough to work well as a single varietal, but also used with Golding clones.
Character: rich and complex aroma profile includes green tea, intense fruit, flowers, grass, herbs and vanilla.
Alpha 4.5-6.5%, beta 2-3.3%, cohumulone 26-30%.
Total oil 0.6-1ml. Myrcene 25-30%, humulene 21-26%, caryophyllene 7.9-8.1%, farnesene 3-5%.
Substitutes: Fuggle, Pioneer.

Sunshine: little-known aroma variety bred at Wye College in the early 1930s, generally an ornamental variety but very similar to its offspring Comet when used in brewing.
Alpha 6.7-8.2%, beta 2.1-3.1%, cohumulone 34%.
Total oil 1.35ml. Myrcene 55%, humulene 0.9%.
Substitute: Comet.

Sussex: distinctive and characterful aroma hop bred in 2005 from a chance find on a farm in Northiam, East Sussex,

where hops had been grown for over a century. Analysis revealed a totally unique oil profile, and brewing use has uncovered a powerful aroma, delicate tropical flavours and great flavour retention. Although classed as an aroma variety, when used early it has a well-rounded bitterness.
Character: delicate tropical flavours and a unique fruity aroma with notes of vanilla.
Alpha 4.3-5.8%, beta 2.4-3.2%, cohumulone 29-32%.
Total oil 0.4-0.6ml. Myrcene 42%, humulene 23%, farnesene <1%.
Substitutes: Progress, Whitbread Golding, Fuggle.

Target aka Wye Target: dual-purpose mainstay of British brewing for over 40 years, Target includes Northern Brewer and Eastwell Golding in its ancestry. Despite its age, this dependable all-rounder now seems to be increasingly popular with craft brewers both in its home country and in North America.
Character: intense herbal and citrus aroma, spicy flavour.
Alpha 8-12.5%, beta 5-5.5%, cohumulone 29-35%.
Total oil 1.6-2.6ml. Myrcene 17-22%, humulene 8-10%, caryophyllene 0-1%, farnesene <1%.
Substitutes: Fuggle, Willamette.

Tolhurst: very traditional old English aroma variety, cultivated in Horsmonden, Kent, in the 1880s. Enjoyed great popularity in the 1920s but has been discontinued in its native land owing to poor growth and storage stability. Still possibly being grown in the USA.
Character: very subdued, might suit a lambic.
Alpha 2.2%, beta 2.9%, cohumulone 31%.
Total oil 0.65ml. Myrcene 42.5%, humulene 19.4%, caryophyllene 7.7%, farnesene 8.3%.

Viking: aroma hop bred at Wye. Cross between an experimental Swedish variety and an unnamed English male; sister to Saxon and grandchild of Bramling Cross and Northdown. When released in 1973 Viking was one of a new wave of modern high-alpha hops bred to control the wilt that plagued Kent at the time. Unfortunately, it didn't show the required tolerance and was considered a failure. However, it was popular with home brewers and is still grown in the US. Bitter enough to make a single hop for sweeter, more full-bodied dark beers.
Character: intensely herbal, spicy and floral.
Alpha 8-10%, beta 4-5%, cohumulone 21-24%.
Total oil 1.16ml. Myrcene 47.3%, humulene 10.5%, caryophyllene 5.3%, farnesene 9.1%.
Substitutes: Saxon, Target, Pilgrim.

Whitbread Golding Variety: aroma hop selected for propagation in 1911 from an open pollination of Bates Brewer on a farm in Kent that was soon afterwards bought by the brewer Whitbread. Gained popularity in the 1950s for its resistance to wilt. Not a true Golding, possibly even descended from Fuggle.
Character: sweet fruit; earthy, floral, herbal and woody aromas.
Alpha 5-7.5%, beta 2.5-3.5%, cohumulone 37%.
Total oils 0.8-1.2ml. Myrcene 24-27%, humulene 38-42%, caryophyllene 9-13%, farnesene 1-2%.
Substitutes: Fuggle, East Kent Golding.

Yeoman: very high-alpha bittering variety bred at Wye in the 1970s. Highly resistant but with a poor yield. No longer grown commercially and therefore hard to come by, but the ancestor of many current varieties including Phoenix,

Pioneer and Australian Superpride.
Character: strong citrus aroma.
Alpha 12-16%, beta 4-5%, cohumulone 25%.
Total oil 1.7-2.4ml. Myrcene 47.9%, humulene 19.8%, caryophyllene 9.5%.

Zenith: disease-resistant high-alpha bittering hop developed at Wye in the 1970s, well suited to traditional bitters.
Character: almost no aroma.
Alpha 9-11%, beta 3%, cohumulone 25%.
Total oil 1.76ml. Myrcene 52%, humulene 18%, caryophyllene 7%.
Substitutes: Northern Brewer, Target.

France

Aramis: originally an aroma hop; now seen as dual-purpose. Crossed in 2002 from Strisselspalt and Whitbread Golding, it was the first result of the Comptoir Agricole breeding programme.
Character: sweet with notes of spice, citrus and herbs.
Alpha 7.9-8.3%, beta 3.8-4.5%, cohumulone 42%.
Total oil 1.2-1.6ml. Myrcene 40%, humulene 21%, caryophyllene 7.4%, farnesene 2-4%.
Substitutes: Willamette, Challenger, Strisselspalt, Centennial, Chinook, Hallertau, Tettnang.

Barbe-Rouge: new aroma variety from the Alsace Comptoir's research and development programme. Still in trials but causing huge excitement among US craft brewers. Recommended for wheatbeers, saisons, sours and even IPAs. Few details released as yet.
Character: creates a subtle red berry aroma and a more dominant strawberry/cherry flavour and finish. Said to be

lacking bitterness.
Alpha 6.6-8%.

Bouclier: dual-purpose cross between Strisselspalt and a
wild male from Wye, Kent, developed in Alsace. Suitable
for bittering mild beers such as saison or Pilsner or as late
addition hops in bitter and full-bodied ales.
Character: herb, grass and spice aromas; citrus and floral
flavours.
Alpha 5.2-9%, beta 2.4-3.3%, cohumulone 20-25%.
Total oil 1.1-1.6ml. Myrcene 38%, humulene 34%.
Substitutes: Tradition, Tettnanger Spalter Select.

Elsaesser: now confined to very limited acreage in Alsace,
Elsaesser is an aroma variety of unknown antiquity and
parentage but seems similar in some ways to Germany's
noble hops.
Character: noble aromas.
Alpha 4.6%, beta 5.7%, cohumulone 20-30%.
Total oil 0.28-1.13ml. Humulene 32%.

Précoce de Bourgogne aka Early Burgundy: near-obsolete
aroma hop, first cloned 1977 but no longer grown
commercially.
Alpha 3.1-3.7%, beta 2.6-3.5%, cohumulone 23%.
Total oil 0.34ml. Myrcene 45%, humulene 20%,
caryophyllene 5.9%, farnesene 10.6%.

Strisselspalt: old-established aroma hop from Alsace, used
mostly in lagers.
Character: floral, herbal and lemony, similar to
Hersbrucker.
Alpha 1.8-5.7%, beta 2.5-6%, cohumulone 20-27%.

Total oil 0.6-0.9ml. Myrcene 35-52%, humulene 12-32%, caryophyllene 8-10.3%, farnesene <1%.
Substitutes: Crystal, Hallertau, Mount Hood, Liberty, Hersbrucker, Southern Cross.

Tardif de Bourgogne: ancient aroma variety grown in Alsace and popular with French brewers; hard to find elsewhere.
Character: mild, European-style aroma.
Alpha 3.1-5.5%, beta 3.1-5.5%, cohumulone 20%.
Total oil 0.49-0.73ml. Myrcene 44%, humulene 13%, caryophyllene 5.7%, farnesene 0.2%.

Triskel: new aroma cultivar of Strisselspalt and Yeoman. One of the first three registered products from the Alsace varietal research programme along with Bouclier and Aramis, all intended to increase Strisselspalt's alpha value without affecting its aroma. Suited to late addition or dry hopping, especially in Belgian or lighter ales.
Character: floral, subtle fruit, citrusy.
Alpha 8-9%, beta 4-4.7%, cohumulone 20-23%.
Total oil 1.5-2ml. Myrcene 60%, humulene 13.5%, caryophyllene 6.1%, farnesene <1%.
Substitutes: Strisselspalt, Ahtanum, Centennial, Chinook, Simcoe.

Germany

Hallertau aka Hallertauer Mittelfrüh: aroma variety; one of the four original noble hops. Low yielding and susceptible to wilt, Hallertauer has been in steady decline for years. It now accounts for only 10 per cent of German plantings, many of them outside its native region, but it is so popular with brewers around the world that it has sired innumerable offspring. Most of them are distinct enough to list as varie-

ties in their own right but some are more or less identical: Hallertauer Gold, for instance, which has a somewhat higher alpha percentage, is no longer even separately marketed.
Character: lightly flowery and spicy.
Alpha 3.5%-5.5% beta 3.5-4.5%, cohumulone 20-26%.
Total oil 0.6-1.2ml. Myrcene 35-44%, humulene 30-55%, caryophyllene 10-15%, farnesene <1%.
Substitutes: Liberty, Tradition.

Hallertau Blanc: complex and versatilearomahop bred at Huell from Cascade, released 2012.
Character: gooseberry flavour similar to Sauvignon Blanc; heady and intense aromas including blackcurrant, elderflower, grapes, grapefruit, lemongrass, passion fruit and pineapple.
Alpha 9-12%, beta 4-6%, cohumulone 22-26%.
Total oil 0.8-1.5ml. Myrcene 50-75%, humulene <3%, caryophyllene <2%, farnesene <3.5%.
Substitutes: Nelson Sauvin.

Hallertauer Herkules: bred from Hallertauer Mittelfrüh via Hallertauer Taurus, Herkules is a high-alpha dual-purpose hop released in 2005.
Character: clean, fruity, spicy aromas of melon, black pepper and pine.
Alpha 12-17%, beta 4-5.5%, cohumulone 32-38%.
Total oil 1.4-2.4ml. Myrcene 30-50%, humulene 28-45%, caryophyllene 7-12%, farnesene <1%.

Hallertauer Magnum: very successful high-alpha hop bred in 1980 at Hüll from Galena and a German male hop.
Character: smooth bitterness, subtle citrus flavours, low aroma.

Alpha 12-14%, beta 4.5-5.5%, cohumulone 24-25%.
Total oil 1.9-2.3ml. Myrcene 30-35%, humulene 34-40%,
caryophyllene 8-12%, farnesene 0-1%.
Substitutes: Hallertauer Taurus, Columbus, Nugget,
Horizon.

Hallertauer Merkur: high-alpha, high-oil hop developed
from Magnum at Hüll, released 2000.
Character: earthy, spicy bitterness, but with a fresh citrus
aroma.
Alpha 12-16.2%, beta 5-7.3%, cohumulone 17.8-19%.
Total oil 2.6-3ml. Myrcene 48-49%, humulene 29-32%,
caryophyllene 8-9%, farnesene <1%.
Substitutes: Magnum.

Hallertauer Taurus: dual-purpose Hallertauer offspring
released 1995; super-high alpha with a uniquely high level
of the antioxidant xanthohumol.
Character: chocolate, banana, spice, pepper, curry.
Alpha 12.3-17.9%, beta 4-6%, cohumulone 23-25%.
Total 0.9-1.5ml. Myrcene 30%, humulene 30-31%, caryo-
phyllene 8%, farnesene <1%.
Substitutes: Magnum, Merkur, Herkules.

Hallertauer Tradition: aroma hop bred from Hallertau
Mittelfrüher, Hallertauer Gold and Saaz for fungus and
disease resistance, released 1991. It has higher alpha, lower
cohumulone and higher myrcene than its parents.
Character: earthy, grassy; luscious fruity aroma.
Alpha 4.6-7%, beta 4-5%, cohumulone 23-29%.
Total oil 0.9-1.9ml. Myrcene 20-25%, humulene 40-55%,
caryophyllene 10-15%, farnesene <1%.
Substitutes: Hallertau Mittlefrüh, Liberty, Ultra, Crystal.

Hersbrucker aka Hersbrucker G, Hersbrucker Spät: aroma hop originally bred as a wilt-resistant successor to Hallertauer Mittelfrüh. Hersbrucker reached the height of its popularity in the 1970s-80s, and annual production still exceeds 1,000 tonnes. Commonly used in lagers, but some British craft brewers now choose it for their ales. Organic Hersbrucker is also available, and a great number of selections such as Hersbrucker Pure have been tested but have never really caught on.

Character: mild fruity, spicy and floral aromas.

Alpha 2-5%, beta 4-6%, cohumulone 19-25%.

Total oil 0.5-1.3ml. Myrcene 10-25%, humulene 15-35%, caryophyllene 7-15%, farnesene 0-1%.

Substitutes: Hallertauer Tradition, Spalt Select, Mount Hood, Strisselspalt, Liberty.

Hersbrucker Red-Stem aka Hersbrucker Alpha: dual-purpose hop introduced in the 1980s but declining in the face of competition from Tradition and Spalter Select.

Character: earthy, herbal noble characteristics.

Alpha 5-6%, beta 5-6%, cohumulone 18%.

Total oil 1.2ml. Myrcene 55%, humulene 10%, caryophyllene 9%, farnesene 17.5%.

Hüll Melon: aroma variety introduced in 2012, an offspring of Cascade. Quirky mixture of flavours and aromas.

Character: intensely fruity, luscious flavours and aromas of melon and strawberry.

Alpha 6.9-7.5%, beta 7.3-7.9%, cohumulone 25-30%.

Total oil 0.8ml. Myrcene 36%, humulene 10-20%, caryophyllene 5-10%, farnesene <1%.

Hüll Bitterer: dual-use varietydeveloped from Northern Brewer as a wilt-resistant hop and released in 1978, now largely superseded by other varieties, especially Perle. Alpha 4.5-7%, beta 4.5-5.5%, cohumulone 26-31%. Total oil 1-1.5ml. Myrcene 28-51%, humulene 9-21%, caryophyllene 5-8%, farnesene <1%.

Mandarina Bavaria: aroma hop developed at Hüll from Cascade, Hallertau Blanc and Hüll Melon; released 2012. **Character:** mandarin orange, citrus. Alpha 8.5-10.5%, beta 5-6.5%, cohumulone 33%. Total oil 2ml. Myrcene 70%, humulene 5%, caryophyllene 2%, farnesene 1%. **Substitutes:** Columbus, Nugget, Cascade.

Opal: dual-purpose variety released by Hüll 2004; respectable alpha level but now mainly used for its aromas. **Character:** sweet, spicy and slightly peppery flavour with a light, clean citrus fruit aroma. Alpha 13-14%, beta 3.5-5.5%, cohumulone 28-34%. Total oil 0.8-1.3ml. Myrcene 30-45%, humulene 20-25%, caryophyllene 9-10%, farnesene <1%. **Substitutes:** East Kent Golding, Styrian Golding.

Orion: old-schooldual-purpose cross between Perle and a German male, with low cohumulone and high myrcene content. Popular in traditional Helles and Pilsner beers, butnoteasy to find outside Germany. **Character:** traditional grassy hop aroma. Alpha 8-9%, beta 4.94-5.73%, cohumulone 25-29%. Total oil 1.8-2.1ml. Myrcene 41-56%, humulene 17-26%, caryophyllene 7-13%, farnesene <1%. **Substitutes:** Perle, Northern Brewer.

Perle: hugely popular dual-purpose variety created from Northern Brewer and a German male, released in 1978 and now grown in many countries.
Character: mint, pine, hint of spice, slightly floral, fruity.
Alpha 8-9%, beta 8%, cohumulone 28%.
Total oil 0.6-1.2ml. Myrcene 44%, humulene 29%, caryophyllene 10.2%, farnesene 0.2%.
Substitutes: Northern Brewer, Hallertauer Mittelfrueh, Mount Hood, Liberty.

Polaris: dual-purpose variety with very high alpha acid, released by Hüll Institute in 2012.
Character: floral and fruity aromas, spice, pine and mint.
Alpha 18-23%, beta 4.5-6%, cohumulone 22-28%.
Total oil 4-5ml. Myrcene 50%, humulene 20-35%, caryophyllene 8-13%, farnesene <1%.

Saphir aka Sapphire: aroma hop bred at Hüll as a more commercial and resistant alternative to Hallertau Mittelfrüh; released 2002.
Character: sweet citrus aromas with tangerine notes.
Alpha 2-4.5%, beta 4-7%, cohumulone 12-17%.
Total oil 0.8-1.4ml. Myrcene 25-40%, humulene 20-30%, caryophyllene 9-14%, farnesene <1%.
Substitutes: Hallertau Mittelfrüh, Tradition, Spalter Select.

Smaragd aka Emerald: like Sapphire, an attempt to produce a more resistant alternative to Hallertauer Mittlefrüh. Bred from Hallertauer Gold at Hüll, released 2007. Low acid, low cohumulone dual-purpose hop with an unusual oil balance, mostly made up of myrcene and farnesene.
Character: predominantly fruity aroma with bold floral notes, flavours of earth and spice.

Alpha 4-6%, beta Acid 3.5-5.5%, cohumulone 13-18%.
Total oil 0.7-1.7ml. Myrcene 20-40%, humulene 30-50%,
caryophyllene 9-14%, farnesene 1%.

Spalt aka Spalter: noble hop said to be one of the world's
oldest varieties. May date back as far as the 8th century.
Still mainly grown in the region near Nuremburg that bears
its name. Despite low yields, Spalt is in high demand.
Character: wood, earth, spice.
Alpha 2.5-5.7%, beta 3-5%, cohumulone 22-29%.
Total oil 0.5-0.9ml. Myrcene 20-35%, humulene 20-30%,
caryophyllene 8-13%, farnesene 12-18%.
Substitutes: Saaz, Tettnanger, Santiam, Liberty, Hallertau
varieties.

Spalter Select: Disease-resistant and high-yield Spalt and
Hallertauer aroma variety bred at Hüll and released in
1993.
Character: spicier than its parents.
Alpha 3-6.5%, beta 2-5%, cohumulone 20-28%.
Total oil 0.5-1.2ml. Myrcene 40-50%, humulene 15-20%,
caryophyllene 6-8%, farnesene 10-22%.
Substitutes: Saaz, Tettnanger, Spalt, Hersbrucker, Perle,
Hallertau Tradition.

Tettnanger: dual-purpose variety; one of the four noble
hops and today grown all over the world. A higher
farnesene content makes Tettnanger noticeably more
aromatic than the other noble hops except perhaps Saaz,
from which it is probably descended.
Character: balanced floral and herbal aromas with some
spiciness.
Alpha 3-5.8%, beta 2.8-5.3%, cohumulone 24%.

Total oil 0.36-1.07ml. Myrcene 40.6%, humulene 20.4%, caryophyllene 6.2%, farnesene 11.3%.
Substitutes: Saaz, Spalter, Santiam, Spalter Select, Tettnanger (US), Crystal.

Ultra: triploid aroma variety bred from Saaz and Hallertau; released 1995. Rich in humulene, suited to Pilsners, wheats and bocks both for finishing and aroma. Oil profile almost identical to Hallertauer Mittelfrüh.
Character: mildly peppery aroma similar to Saaz.
Alpha 3-5%, beta 3.6-5%, cohumulone 25-35%.
Total oil 0.8-1.5ml. Myrcene 25-35%, humulene 30-40%, caryophyllene 10-15%, farnesene 0-1%.
Substitutes: Crystal, Tettnanger, Saaz, Hallertauer Tradition, Liberty.

Wüertemburger: old German noble aroma hop, no longer grown commercially due to its low vigour and poor yield.
Character: noble aroma.
Alpha 5%, beta 4%, cohumulone 28%.
Total oil 1.25ml. Myrcene 59%, humulene 18%, caryophyllene 6%, farnesene 4%.

Japan

Eastern Gold: super-alpha developed by Kirin Brewing from Kirin No.2 and an open-pollinated wild American hop. Despite its yield potential, highalpha content and storage stability, it seems it is not currently being grown in any quantity. Eastern Green, Kirin's attempt at breeding a super-alpha from an open pollination with Toyomidori, has met with a similar lack of success.
Alpha 11-14%, beta 5-6%, cohumulone 27%.
Total oil 1.43ml. Myrcene 42%, humulene 19%,

caryophyllene 7-8%, farnesene 3%.
Substitutes: Kirin No.2, Brewer's Gold.

Furano Ace: aroma variety developed in the 1980s by Sapporo Brewery; a cross between Brewer's Gold and Saaz. Showed much early promise but ultimately failed to compete with modern high-alpha varieties despite a very unusual oil composition. A large family of offspring and descendants includes Furano 6, 18, Beauty, Beta, Laura, Little Star, Royal Greenand Special.
Character: noble.
Alpha 7-8%, beta 5-8%, cohumulone 21%.
Total oil 1.53ml. Myrcene 50%, humulene 19%, caryophyllene 7%, farnesene 12%.

Golden Star: mutant form of Shinshuwase selected in the 1960s by Sapporo as a higher yield and more mildew-resistant aroma hop. Descended from Saaz and White Vine.
Alpha 5.4%, beta 4.6%, cohumulone 50%.
Total oil 0.63ml. Myrcene 57%, humulene 13%, caryophyllene 5%.
Substitute: Saaz.

Kirin No 2: dual-purpose variety developed by Kirin Brewery as a clonal selection from Shinshuwase, and therefore a descendant of Saaz.
Alpha 6.8-10.3%, beta 5.2-8%, cohumulone 43-45%.
Total oil 1.18ml. Myrcene 50%, humulene 14%, caryophyllene 9.4%, farnesene 0.2%.

Kaikogane: aroma hop bred by Kirin, released 1980. Variant of Shinshuwase.

Kitamidori: high-alpha variety developed from a seedling selection made at Kirin in the 1980s. Never grown commercially.
Alpha 9-12%, beta 5-6%, cohumulone 22%.
Total oil 1.35ml. Myrcene 34%, humulene 31%, caryophyllene 8-10%, farnesene 6-7%.

Shinshuwase: high-yielding aroma hop dating back a century or more. A cross between Saaz and White Vine, Shinshuwase was used as a bittering hop until the introduction of super alpha varieties. Still grown, but mostly succeeded by Kirin No 2, Toyomidori, Kitamidori and Eastern Gold.
Character: lemon aroma.
Alpha 4.7-8.3%, beta 4-6.1%, cohumulone 51%.
Total oil 0.42-0.98ml. Myrcene 57.5%, humulene 12%, caryophyllene 20.3%, farnesene 0.1%.
Substitutes: Saaz, Hallertau, Santiam.

Sorachi Ace: dual-purpose cross between Saaz, Brewer's Gold and Beikei produced by Sapporo in the 1980s; currently enjoying a resurgence in the US.
Character: flavours of lemon, orange, dill, bubblegum, coriander and oak.
Alpha 11.5-16%, beta 6-7.5%, cohumulone 23-28%.
Total oil 1.5-3ml. Myrcene 44-55%, humulene 20-26%, caryophyllene 7-11%, farnesene 2-5%.

Toyomidori: produced by Kirin and released in 1990, Toyomidori was developed alongside Kitamidori and Eastern Gold as a high alpha variety but was the least successful of the three and has been largely discontinued due to problems with downy mildew. A cross between Northern

Brewer and a Wye male, it is also a parent of Azacca.
Alpha 11-13%, beta 5-6%, cohumulone 40%.
Total oil 1.06ml. Myrcene 59%, humulene 9-12%, caryo-
phyllene 4-5%, farnesene trace.

New Zealand

Dr Rudi: originally known as Super Alpha on its release in
1976 and renamed in 2012, Dr Rudi was bred from Smooth
Cone and was intended as a bittering hop. It is now regard-
ed as dual-purpose and works well in single-hopped beers.
Character: grass, pine, herbal and citrus.
Alpha 10-12%, beta 7-8.5%, cohumulone 36-39%.
Total oil 1.3-1.6ml. Myrcene 29-48%, humulene 22-33%,
farnesene <1%.
Substitutes: Green Bullet.

Green Bullet: high-alpha hop released in 1972, bred by open
cross-pollination of Smooth Cone. New Zealand's most
common bittering hop, it also has an interesting aroma
profile and can contribute Styrian-like spiciness as a late
kettle addition.
Character: aromas of raisin and fruit, high-alpha zing but a
smooth taste due to myrcene content.
Alpha 11-14%, beta 6.5-7%, cohumulone 38-39%.
Total oil 0.46-1.13ml. Myrcene 38.3%, humulene 28.2%,
caryophyllene 9.2%, farnesene 0.3%.

Hallertau Aroma aka Wakatu: disease resistant aroma hop
bred from Hallertauer Mittlefrüh open-pollinated by a New
Zealand-derived male, which has altered the aroma and
flavour so much that it is no longer considered a true Hallertau. Also used nowadays as a single-varietal dual-purpose
hop. Released 1988.

Character: clean taste, notes of lime zest, floral bouquet.
Alpha 7-9%, beta 5.8-8.5%, cohumulone 28-35%.
Total oil 0.9-1.1ml. Myrcene 35-48%, humulene 10-16.8%,
caryophyllene 8%, farnesene 5-6.7%.
Substitutes: Hallertauer Mittelfrüh, Perle.

Kohatu: single-varietal dual-purpose variety released alongside Wai-iti in 2011. Intense aromas, but also good bittering
qualities, it is the descendant of Hallertauer Mittelfrueh.
Character: intense tropical fruit and pine needle aroma.
Alpha 6-8.1%, beta 4-6%, cohumulone 21%.
Total oil 0.12-1ml. Myrcene 35.5%, humulene 36.5%, caryophyllene 11.5%, farnesene 0.3%.

Motueka aka Belgian Saaz: dual-purpose triploid bred from
Saaz and an unnamed native breeding strain. Equally suited
to light, fresh lagers and maltier, heavier ales.
Character: tropical fruit and lemon-lime citrus.
Alpha 6.5-8.5%, beta 5-5.5%, cohumulone 29%.
Total oil 0.8ml. Myrcene 47.7%, humulene 3.6%, caryo-
phyllene 2%, farnesene 12.2%.
Substitutes: Saaz, Saaz (US), Sterling.

Nelson Sauvin: dual-purpose variety named in honour of
New Zealand's most successful grape, the Sauvignon Blanc,
with which it shares many characteristics. Descended from
Smooth Cone and released in 2000, it hasn't exactly been
a huge success with the mainstream but has received an
enthusiastic welcome from craftand home brewers. Note
the complex oil profile.
Character: smooth bittering; rich, fruity, gooseberry and
passion fruit flavours and aromas.
Alpha 12-13%, beta 6-8%, cohumulone 24%.

Total oil 1.1ml. Myrcene 22.2%, humulene 36.4%, caryo-phyllene 10.7%, farnesene 0.4%.
Substitutes: Pacific Jade, Pacifica.

Orbit: constantly evolving blend of dual-purpose hops from New Zealand's 'hops with a difference' breeding programme. The selection changes from year to year based on the character and quality of the available crops, so specific tasting notes are impossible. Past blends have been noted for their flavours and aromas of tropical fruit.
Alpha 4-6%, beta 4-6%, cohumulone 25%.
Total oil 1.5ml. Myrcene 33%, humulene 33%, caryophyl-lene 14%, farnesene 2%.
Substitutes: Pacifica.

Pacific Gem: good dual-purpose cross between Smooth Cone, California Late Cluster and Fuggle released in 1987, it is used around the world in various styles but most notably in European lagers.
Character: notes of oak and blackberry
Alpha 13-16%, beta 7-9%, cohumulone 37-40%.
Total oil 1.2-1.4ml. Myrcene 33-55%, humulene 18-30%, caryophyllene 7-11%, farnesene <1%.
Substitutes: Fuggle.

Pacific Jade: high-alpha bittering hop with distinctive fresh aromas, bred from Saaz and First Choice. It was released 2004 and is now finding its way into inventories worldwide.
Character: lemon citrus and black pepper.
Alpha 12-14%, beta 7-8%, cohumulone 24%.
Total oil 1.4ml. Myrcene 33.3%, humulene 32.9%, caryo-phyllene 10.2%, farnesene 0.3%.
Substitutes: Magnum.

Pacific Sunrise: bittering variety released in 2000, the result of a complicated cross including California Late Cluster and Fuggle. Alongside its powerful bittering quality sits a high myrcene percentage, ensuring characterful aromas and flavours in everything from lager to brown ale.
Character: herbal and piney aromas.
Alpha 12.5-14.5%, beta 6-6.5%, cohumulone 27-30%.
Total oil 1.7-2ml. Myrcene 45-55%, humulene 19-25%, caryophyllene 6-9%, farnesene 0-1%.
Substitutes: Pacific Gem.

Pacifica aka Pacific Hallertau: triploid aroma hop resulting from an open pollination breeding of Hallertauer Mittel-früh. Released 1994.
Character: citrus, spicy, orange marmalade and floral aromas.
Alpha 5-6%, beta 6%, cohumulone 25%.
Total oil 1ml. Myrcene 12.5%, humulene 50.9%, caryophyllene 16.7%, farnesene 0.2%.
Substitutes: Liberty.

Rakau aka Alpha Aroma: bred in the late 1970s from Smooth Cone and released in 1983, Rakau is a dual-purpose variety whose high concentration of myrcene makes it ideal for dry-hopping highly perfumed beers such as American-style pale ales.
Character: firm bitterness; tropical fruit aromas of passion-flower and peach.
Alpha 5.8-10.9%, beta 2.6-4.8%, cohumulone 27%.
Total oil 1.21ml. Myrcene 44-65%, humulene 15%, caryophyllene 3-8%, farnesene 5%.

Riwaka aka D Saaz: a firm favourite aroma variety among New Zealand's craft brewers, Riwaka's oil content is nearly double that of parent Saaz. That and a near 1:1 ratio of alpha to beta make it, according to one fan, the ultimate aroma variety for hoppy beers. A product of HortResearch's New Zealand 'hops with a difference' programme, released 1997.
Character: strong sweet notes of grapefruit and kumquat.
Alpha 4.5-6.5%, beta 4-5%, cohumulone 29-36%.
Total oil 0.8mg. Myrcene 68%, humulene 9%, caryophyllene 4%, farnesene 1%.
Substitutes: Saaz.

Smooth Cone: dual-purpose hop bred along with First Choice and Calicross in the 1960s to combat black root rot. Offspring of California Cluster and parent of many much higher-alpha modern varieties. No longer grown commercially but can still be found.
Alpha 7-9.5%, beta 3.4-5.2%, cohumulone 31%.
Total oil 0.38-1.14ml. Myrcene 55%, humulene 21%, caryophyllene 6%, farnesene 0-1%.
Substitutes: Cluster.

Southern Cross: hugely successful dual-purpose cross between Smooth Cone and Fuggle, released 1994. A mellow bitterness makes it a good early addition; as a late addition, it's a star.
Character: soft bitterness; heady lemon peel, pine needles and spicy flavours and aromas.
Alpha 13-14%, beta 6-7%, cohumulone 28%.
Total oil 1.59ml. Myrcene 58%, humulene 14%, caryophyllene 4%, farnesene 5%.

Sticklebract: triploid black root rot-resistant high-alpha variety bred from an open pollinated First Choice; released 1972.
Character: pine and citrus.
Alpha 13-14.2%, beta 7.5-8.5%, cohumulone 40-45%.
Total oil 0.76-1.72ml. Myrcene 51-64%, humulene 8-11%, caryophyllene 3-6%, farnesene 4-4.6%.
Substitutes: Northern Brewer.

Wai-iti: aroma hop with Hallertauer Mittlefrüh and Liberty in its ancestry. Released 2011 alongside Kohatu; similar to Riwaka.
Character: fresh lemon, lime zest, mandarin and stone fruit.
Alpha 2.5-3.5%, beta 4.5-5.5%, cohumulone 22-24%.
Total oil 1.6ml. Myrcene 30%, humulene 28%, caryophyllene 9%, farnesene 13%.
Substitutes: Riwaka.

Waimea: dual-purpose variety released in 2012, with Californian Late Cluster, Pacific Jade, Fuggle and Saaz in its ancestry.
Character: citrus and pine.
Alpha 16-19%, beta 7-9%.
Total oil 2.1ml. Myrcene 60%, humulene 10%, caryophyllene 3%, farnesene 5%.
Substitutes: Columbus

North America

Ahtanum: Yakima Chief Ranches aroma hop named after the site where Charles Carpenter established the Yakima Valley's first hop farm in 1869.
Character: earthy/floral with pine, lemon and grapefruit

Alpha 4-6.3%, beta 5-6.5%, cohumulone 30-35%.
Total oil 0.8-1.2ml. Myrcene 50-55%, humulene 16-20%, caryophyllene 9-12%, farnesene 0-1%.
Substitutes: Cascade, Amarillo, Simcoe, Centennial, Willamette.

Amallia: dual-purpose neomexicanus varietal considered well suited to brown or dark ales for both bittering and aroma. Still being trialled by Montana State University researchers at time of writing.
Character: deep earthy aroma with pronounced orange citrus flavours.
Alpha 5.5-9%, beta 4.2-8.3%.
Total oil 1ml. Myrcene 80%, humulene 15%, caryophyllene 4.8%, geraniol 1.5%, linalool 0.7%, pinene 0.7%.

Amarillo aka Amarillo Gold: popular dual-purpose hop with ultra-high myrcene content creating a distinctive soft aroma and high alpha level perfect for British-style bitters and strong bitters. Discovered growing wild in one of Virgil Gamache Farm hop yards and also known as VGXP01 in honour of Virgil Gamache, the patriarch of the family.
Character: orange citrus flavour; flowery, spicy aromas.
Alpha 8-11%, beta 6-7%, cohumulone 21-24%.
Total oil 1.5-1.9ml. Myrcene 68-70%, humulene 9-11%, caryophyllene 2-4%, farnesene 2-4%.
Substitutes: Cascade, Centennial, Summit, Ahtanum, Chinook, Saaz.

Apollo: mildew-resistant super-alpha released in 2006. Descended from Zeus and two unnamed USDA varieties crossed at Golden Gate Roza Hop Ranch in Washington State. Usually combined with aroma hops for balance but

can also go solo as a late addition or dry hop.
Character: sharp, clean bittering; grapefruit notes.
Alpha 15-20%, beta 5.5-8%, cohumulone 23-28%.
Total oil 1.5-2.5ml. Myrcene 30-50%, humulene 20-35%,
caryophyllene 14-20%, farnesene 1%.
Substitutes: Nugget, Columbus, Zeus, Magnum,
Millennium.

Aquila: aroma variety selected from an open pollination
of Brewer's Gold in 1980 and released 1994; discontinued
1996 after losing Anheuser-Busch's backing.
Alpha 6.7-8.9%, beta 4.1-4.9%, cohumulone 46%.
Total oil 1.45ml.

Armadillo: experimental aroma variety from Yakima Valley
Hops. Early brewing trials suggest it can overpower other
hops unless used sparingly, but poor storage stability is
reported as a potential handicap.
Character: flavours and aromas of tropical fruit, citrus,
pine and melon.
Alpha 5.9%, beta 3.2%.

Azacca: characterful dual-purpose hop bred directly from
Toyomidori; ancestry also includes Summit and Northern
Brewer. High in alpha acids, but with complex aromas and
flavours too.
Character: aromas of tropical fruit and citrus including
mango, papaya, pineapple, tangerine, orange, lemon and
grapefruit; spice, grass and pine on the palate.
Alpha 14-16%, beta 4-5.5%, cohumulone 38-45%.
Total oil 1.6-2.5ml. Myrcene 46-55%, humulene 14-18%,
caryophyllene 8-12%.

Banner: more or less obsolete 1970s bittering offshoot of Brewer's Gold, abandoned for its susceptibility to mildew and poor storage ability. Revived for abortive tests by Anheuser-Busch in 1990s. Sibling to Aquila.
Alpha 9-13%, beta 5.3-8%, cohumulone 34%.
Total oil 2.17ml. Myrcene 66.4%, humulene 11.8%, caryophyllene 7.7%.
Substitutes: Aquila, Cluster, Galena.

Belma: dual-purpose variety released by Hops Direct and Puterbaugh Farms in the Yakima Valley in 2012. High myrcene and low humulene content.
Character: a cocktail of orange, melon, strawberry, pineapple and grapefruit.
Alpha 9.4-12.1%.
Total oil 0.8ml. Myrcene 66%, humulene 13.77%, caryophyllene 1.64%.

Bianca aka Bianco, Bianca Gold: With its lemon-yellow leaves and red-brown to pink contrasting stem, Bianca was bred as an ornamental hop and needs semi-shaded areas as it is vulnerable to leaf-burn in direct sunlight. While not bred for brewing, the cones can be used as late hops for a novel alternative to Saaz. Sunbeam, Bianca's half-sister, is very similar.
Alpha 7-8%, beta 3.4%, cohumulone 20-28%.
Total oil 0.6-1ml. Myrcene 30%, humulene 25%, caryophyllene 8%, farnesene 13%.
Substitutes: Saaz, Sunbeam.

Bitter Gold: Super-alpha variety released in 1999. Bitter Gold's ancestry includes Bullion, Brewer's Gold, Comet, and Fuggle. Its alpha content is higher than any of its parents and higher even than Galena or Nugget. Released for production in 1999, Bitter Gold is quite versatile and can be used as a bittering or flavour addition, imparting strong flavours reminiscent of stone fruit, watermelon and pear.

Character: flavours of stone fruit, watermelon and pear; very faint grassy aroma.

Alpha 15.4-18.8%, beta 6.1-8%, cohumulone 36-41%.

Total oil 0.81-3.92ml. Myrcene 68.2%, humulene 7.5%, caryophyllene 8.4%, farnesene 1.2%.

Substitutes: Galena, Nugget.

Bravo: super high-alpha variety developed from Zeus by the Hopsteiner Breeding Programme, released 2006. It has good resistance to powdery mildew.

Character: spicy, earthy, fruity and lightly floral aroma; orange and stone fruit flavours.

Alpha 14-17%, beta 3-5%, cohumulone 29-34%.

Total oil 1.6-2.4ml. Myrcene 25-50%, humulene 18-20%, caryophyllene 10-12%, farnesene 0-1%.

Substitutes: Columbus, Zeus, Apollo, Magnum, Nugget.

Brewer's Gold (US): bittering hop, a higher-alpha cultivar of the original English variety. Widely grown, mainly in Oregon, until the arrival of true super-alphas in the 1980s rendered it commercially redundant. Still grown on a small scale, mainly for the homebrew market.

Character: notes of spice and blackcurrant.

Alpha 8.1-13.1%, beta 3.7-6.8%, cohumulone 41%.

Total oil 1.8ml. Myrcene 40%, humulene 35%, caryophyllene 35%.

Substitutes: Bullion, Cascade, Galena, Northern Brewer, Northdown.

Buzz Bullets: a proprietary dual-purpose blend created by Yakima Valley Hops, still undergoing trials.
Character: clean bitterness; floral, fruity and citrus notes. Alpha 8-10%.

Calicross: 1960s cross between Fuggles and California Cluster; dominant for 20 years for its versatility until super-seded by modern higher-alpha varieties. Mid-level bittering better suited to traditional ales than to the lagers and very pale ales of today. Very high myrcene.
Character: soft, floral aroma.
Alpha 7%, beta 5.6%, cohumulone 38%.
Total oil 0.81ml. Myrcene 61.3%, humulene 13.2%, caryo-phyllene 9.2%, farnesene 2.1%.
Substitutes: Cluster, Fuggles.

Caliente: new dual-purpose hop well received by the US craft brewers for its complexity and versatility.
Character: subdued liquorice, cherry, citrus, peach and pine flavours; stone fruit and mandarin aromas.
Alpha 15.3%, beta 4.3%, cohumulone 35%.
Total oil 1.9ml.

Calypso: Yakima Valley-bred dual-purpose diploid. Despite its origins as an aroma hop, it also has a high alpha content.
Character: crisp, fruity aroma; flavours of apples, pears, stone fruit, lime and tea.
Alpha 12-14%, beta 5-6%, cohumulone 40-42%.
Total oil 1.6-2.5ml. Myrcene 30-45%, humulene 20-35%, caryophyllene 9-15%.

Canadian Redvine: little-known aroma variety whose exact origins are obscure – possibly a native American. Almost

extinct thanks to its susceptibility to mildew and off-flavours until recently, when its hardihood and heavy crop-
ping attracted the attention of researchers. The strain is
currently being improved.
Character: mild cherry flavour, grapefruit peel aroma.
Alpha 5%, beta 5-6%, cohumulone 47%.
Total oil 11.2ml. Myrcene 70%, humulene 2%, caryophyllene 2%, farnesene 4-7%.
Substitutes: Newport, Magnum, Galena.

Cascade: dual-purpose variety developed in the 1950s at
Oregon State University from Fuggle and Serebrianka,
Cascade has gone on to become one of the most popular
American hops of all time. Released in 1972, Cascade now
represents around 10 per cent of all hops produced in the
US and is grown around the world, especially in Australia
and New Zealand but also in Argentina.One of the 'Three
Cs' along with Centennial and Columbus.
Character: floral, spicy, citric with a pronounced note of
grapefruit.
Alpha 4.5-8.9%, beta 3.6-7.5%, cohumulone 33-40%.
Total oil 0.8-1.5ml. Myrcene 45-60%, humulene 8-16%,
caryophyllene 4-6%, farnesene 4%-8%.
Substitutes: Centennial, Amarillo, Columbus, Ahtanum.

Cashmere: smooth dual-purpose variety developed at
Washington State University and released in 2013, Cash-
mere is the result of a marriage of Cascade and Northern
Brewer.
Character: herbal, spicy and melon flavours with lemon
and lime aromas.
Alpha 7.7-9.1%, beta 3.3-7.1%, cohumulone 22-24%.
Total oils 1.2-1.2ml. Myrcene 39-42%, humulene 26-29%,

caryophyllene 11.5-13%, farnesene <1%.
Substitutes: Cascade, Northern Brewer.

Centennial: one of the 'Three Cs' along with Cascade
and Columbus. Centennial is often referred to as 'Super
Cascade' for its well-balanced bitterness and strong aroma.
Versatile dual-purpose hop bred from Brewer's Gold,
Fuggle, East Kent Golding and Bavarian hops at Washington State University, released in 1990.
Character: earthy and floral with an element of citrus.
Alpha 9.5-11.5%, beta 3.5-4.5%, cohumulone 28-30%.
Total oil 1.5-2.5ml. Myrcene 45-55%, humulene 10-18%,
caryophyllene 5-8%, farnesene 0-1%.
Substitutes: Chinook, Galena, Nugget, Zeus, Columbus,
Cascade.

Chama: one of the new neomexicanus strains grown since
2012 on a small scale by the Benedictines of the Monastery
of Christ in the Desert in Abiquiú, New Mexico. Little data
is available but Chama is said to have a citrus, herby and
fruity character; alpha 7.3%, beta 8.2%. Other varieties
from the monastery include Latir: flowery, spicy, herbal;
alpha 7.2%, beta 5%; Mintras: herbal, minty; alpha 4.1%,
beta 6.2%; Tierra: minty, citrus, grassy; alpha 5.7%, beta
6.2%.

Chelan: high-alpha variety but with a very high percentage
of beta acids too. Developed by John I Haas Inc breeding
programme, released 1994. Daughter of Galena, popular in
American-style ales.
Character: strong bitterness from high beta content.
Alpha 12-15.5%, beta 8.5-11.5%, cohumulone 33-35%.
Total oil 1.5-1.9ml. Myrcene 45-55%, humulene 12-15%,

caryophyllene 9-12%, farnesene <1%.
Substitutes: Galena, Nugget.

Chinook: dual-purpose descendant of Petham Golding.
Released 1985, growing in popularity among craft brewers.
Character: pine and spice aromas with grapefruit flavour.
Alpha 12-14%, beta 3-4%, cohumulone 29-34%.
Total oil 1.5-2.7ml. Myrcene 35-40%, humulene 18-25%,
caryophyllene 9-11%, farnesene 0-1%.
Substitutes: Galena, Eroica, Nugget, Bullion, Columbus,
Northern Brewer, Target, Southern Cross, Sticklebract.

Citra: world-beating bittering hop created by John I Haas
Inc/Select Botanicals Group joint venture The Hop Breeding Company; released 2008. Citra's strong, heady citrus
character soon made it one of the most popular high-im-
pact aroma hops in the US, particularly among craft
brewers, although its bittering qualities are seen by many as
being too harsh. Ancestry includes Hallertauer Mittelfrüh,
US Tettnang, Brewer's Gold and EastKent Golding.
Character: powerful aroma and flavour of grapefruit, lime,
tropical fruits.
Alpha 10-15%, beta 3-4.5%, cohumulone 20-35%.
Total oil 1.5-3ml. Myrcene 60-70%, humulene 7-12%, caryophyllene 5-8%, farnesene 1%.
Substitutes: Simcoe, Cascade, Centennial, Mosaic.

Cluster (US) aka Golden Cluster: one of America's oldest and
most popular varieties thanks to its balanced aroma and
bittering qualities. Arose from the hybridisation of varieties imported by English and Dutch settlers from the late
17th century onwards, with indigenous strains. Reputedly
accounted for 96 per cent of the country's total acreage in

the early 20th century and stayed at the top until the 1970s. Local variants include California Cluster, thought extinct but recently revived by Hops-Meister under the names Ivanhoe and Goliath, Yakima Cluster, Late Cluster and others.

Character: Clean, neutral, slightly floral; hint of blackcurrant.

Alpha 5.5-9%, beta 4-6%, cohumulone 36-42%.

Total oil 0.4-1ml. Myrcene 38-55%, humulene 15-20%, caryophyllene 6-10%, farnesene 0-1%.

Substitutes: Eroica, Galena, Brewer's Gold.

Columbia: 1980s aroma variety whose commercial production was discontinued in favour of its sibling Willamette; reintroduced 2011 after craft brewers discovered its pungent kick.

Character: earthy, fruity, like Fuggle with a twist of lemon.

Alpha 8.8%, beta 4%, cohumulone 40%.

Total oil 1-2ml. Myrcene 55%, humulene 17%, caryophyllene 7%, farnesene 4.1%.

Columbus aka Tomahawk aka CTZ: Columbus and Tomahawk are actually the same variety, bred by the USDA in the 1970s and the subject of an ownership dispute between Hopunion and Yakima Chief. In the end it was registered to both, with Hopunion's product recorded as Columbus and Yakima Chief's as Tomahawk. CTZ is a generic name for both, along with the similar Zeus. Bred as a bittering variety but now more commonly used as a late addition. One of the 'Three Cs' with Cascade and Centennial.

Character: resinous; herbal aroma with notes of citrus.

Alpha 14-18%, beta 4.5-6%, cohumulone 28-35%.

Total oil 1.5-4.5ml. Myrcene 25-55%, humulene 9-25%,

caryophyllene 6-12%, farnesene <1%.
Substitutes: Zeus, Chinook, Northern Brewer, Nugget, Target, Warrior, Millennium, Bullion.

Comet: a cross between Sunshine and a native American hop released in 1974 to meet demand for new high-alpha varieties. No longer in commercial production and somewhat hard to find, but still in demand as much for its aromas as for its bittering qualities.
Character: strong grapefruit aroma, dark resin flavours.
Alpha 9.4-12.4%, beta 3-6.1%, cohumulone 41%.
Total oil 1.98ml. Myrcene 67%, humulene 1%, caryophyllene 10%, farnesene 0.1%.
Substitutes: Galena, Summit.

Crystal: triploid aroma variety developed in 1993 from Hallertau, Cascade, Brewer's Gold and Early Green.
Character: woody, floral and fruity with notes of cinnamon, nutmeg and black pepper.
Alpha 2.8-4.4%, beta 5.8-7%, cohumulone 21-26%.
Total oil 0.82ml. Myrcene 47%, humulene 26%, caryophyllene 7%.
Substitutes: Liberty, Mount Hood, Hallertau, Ultra, Strisselspalt, Hersbrucker.

Delta: aroma variety released in 2009, Delta is a Fuggle-type hopsimilar to Willamette with moderate bittering qualities.
Character: spicy with intense melon and citrus aromas.
Alpha 5.5-7%, beta 5.5-7%, cohumulone 22-24%.
Total oil 0.5-1.1ml. Myrcene 25-40%, humulene 25-35%, caryophyllene 9-15%, farnesene 0-1%.
Substitutes: Cascade, Nelson Sauvin, Fuggle, Willamette.

Denali aka Nuggetzilla: new and extraordinary aroma variety from Hopsteiner, descended from Nugget – hence the nickname. Its oil levels are high enough, according to test-brewers, to weep out of compressed blocks of leaf, while its strength of flavour and aroma can be overwhelming.
Character: clean bitterness; fruit cocktail of both tropical and citrus fruits overlaid with notes of stone fruit and apple/pear.
Alpha 14.9%, beta 4-5%, cohumulone 22-25%.
Total oil 4ml. Myrcene 55%, humulene 16%, caryophyllene 6%, farnesene 0.23%.

Ekuanot aka Equinox: aroma hop developed by The Hop Breeding Company in Washington State and released in 2014 to universal acclaim thanks to its oil profile, which creates an astonishingly complex and versatile array of aromas and flavours. Also has a reasonable alpha content. Widely used in pale, light-bodied beers.
Character: fruity aromas including melon, berry, orange peel, lime, lemon, papaya; herbal, peppery, spicy, piney flavours.
Alpha 13-15.5%, beta 4-5.5%, cohumulone 31-36%.
Total oils 2.5-4ml. Myrcene 30-45%, humulene 12-20%, caryophyllene 8-12%, farnesene <1%, B-pinene 0.4-0.8%, linalool 0.2-0.5%, geraniol 0.2%.
Substitutes: Citra, Galaxy.

El Dorado: dual-purpose variety released in 2010; a product of the Yakima Valley's cool climate. Intensely bitter, but it's the richly fruity flavour and aroma that have made it such a big hit with craft brewers.
Character: flavours of tropical fruit, pineapple, mango;

aromas of pear, watermelon, stone fruit and sweets.
Alpha 13-17%, beta 7-8%, cohumulone 28-33%.
Total oil 2.5-3.3ml. Myrcene 55-60%, humulene 10-15%,
caryophyllene 6-8%, farnesene 0.1%.
Substitutes: Galena, Simcoe.

Eroica: bittering hop bred in 1968 from Brewers Gold;
sibling of the more popular Galena. Released 1979 and
much used in wheat beers, but now hard to find.
Character: strongly catty bitterness; spicy, fruity aroma.
Alpha 12-14%, beta 3-5.3%, cohumulone 40-60%.
Total oil 0.8-1.3ml. Myrcene 55-65%, humulene <1%, cary-
ophyllene 7-13%, farnesene <1%.
Substitutes: Bullion, Brewer's Gold, Galena, Glacier,
Nugget, Olympic.

Eureka: dual-purpose variety bred from Apollo and
Merkur; similar to Simcoe and Summit. Strong bittering
qualities and a complex and robust flavour and aroma
profile.
Character: citrus, resin, peach and pine flavours; stone
fruit and mandarin aromas.
Alpha 18-19%, beta 5-6%, cohumulone 27%.
Total oil 3.1ml. Myrcene 43%, humulene 29.8%, caryophyllene 14.2%, farnesene 0.2%.

Falconer's Flight: dual-purpose pelleted blend of Pacific
Northwest hops including Cascade, Centennial, Chinook,
Citra, Cluster, Columbus and Crystal, as well as Hopunion
experimental strains. Launched in 2010 and suitable for
IPAs, pale ales and lagers. Named in memory of Rogue and
Wild Duck brewer Glen Hay Falconer, who died in a road
accident in 2002. Profits go to the Glen Hay Falconer

Foundation, as do the profits from a second Hopunion pelleted blend, Falconer's Flight 7C.
Character: distinctive floral tropical fruit, lemon and grapefruit flavours and aromas.
Alpha 9.5-12%, beta 4-5%, cohumulone 20-25%.
Total oil 1.6-4.6ml.
Substitutes: Cascade, Columbus, Centennial.

Fantasia: proprietary dual-purpose blend from the Barth-Haas group. Claims to taste and smell of cream and caramel. See also TNT and Yellow Sub.
Character: noble aroma with a hint of fruit.
Alpha 4.3%.
Total oil 0.9ml.

Fuggle (US): aroma variety once widely planted in the Pacific Northwest; now largely superseded by its close relative Willamette.
Alpha 4-5.5%, beta 1.5-2%, cohumulone 25-33%.
Total oil 0.7-1.4ml. Myrcene 24-28%, humulene 35-40%, caryophyllene 11-13%, farnesene 4-5%.
Substitutes: Fuggle, Willamette, Styrian Golding, Tettnanger (GR).

Galena: bred from Brewer's Gold in the 1960s to correct Cluster's perceived cattiness, Galena is an excellent dual-purpose variety whose high acid percentages have also made it America's most widely used bittering hop.
Character: fruity aroma.
Alpha 11-13.5%, beta 7.5%, cohumulone 39%.
Total oil 0.9-1.3ml. Myrcene 55-60%, humulene 10-15%, caryophyllene 3-6%, farnesene <1%.

Substitutes: Nugget, Columbus, Zeus, Chinook, Pride of Ringwood, Eroica, Newport, Cluster, Brewers Gold.

Gargoyle: *see* Cluster.

Glacier: dual-purpose hop released by Washington State University in 2000, whose low cohumulone levels make for a moderate bitterness. Bred from Elsasser, Northern Brewer and Brewer's Gold.
Character: herbs, wood and citrus.
Alpha 3.3-9.7%, beta 5.4-10%, cohumulone 11-16%.
Total oil 0.7-1.6ml. Myrcene 33-62%, humulene 24-36%, caryophyllene 7-13%, farnesene 0-1%.
Substitutes: Willamette, Fuggle (US), Tettnanger (GR), Golding (US).

Golding (US): aroma hop descended from East Kent Golding via British Columbia where the variety was first planted but is no longer grown for commercial use. Now widespread in US Pacific North-West where it is used in British and Belgian-style ales.
Character: delicate fruit and herb aromas.
Alpha 4-6%, beta 2-3%, cohumulone 20%.
Total oil 0.4-1ml. Myrcene 25-35%, humulene 35-45%, farnesene <1%.
Substitutes: East Kent Golding, Fuggle, Willamette, Savin-jski Golding, Progress, Whitbread Golding.

Greenburg: dual-purpose hop from Idaho, much favoured by microbreweries. Its beta acids exceed its alpha content.
Character: fruity, woody aromas.
Alpha 5.2%, beta 7.2%.

Hallertau (US): elegant, delicate aroma hop popular with craft brewers.
Character: mildly floral, lightly spiced.
Alpha 3.5-5.5%, beta 3.5-5.5%, cohumulone 18-24%.
Total oil 0.6-1ml. Myrcene 35-44%, humulene 30-38%, caryophyllene 10-12%, farnesene <1%.
Substitutes: Mount Hood, Liberty, Crystal, Hallertauer Mittelfrüh, Hallertauer Tradition, Ultra.

HBC Experimental varieties: the Hop Breeding Company is a joint venture between John I Haas and Select Botanicals Group that releases an unending stream of experimental varieties, each identified by a three-digit number. Those that catch on are formally named, and include the world-beating Citra and more recent hits such as Loral (HBC 291), Ekuanot (HBC 366) and Mosaic (HBC 396). Examples enjoying their baptisms of fire on the open market at time of writing are HBC 431, a fruity and earthy dual-purpose with high alpha acids, myrcene and humulene; HBC 438, another dual-purpose with an alpha percentage of 12.4-14.9% and a myrcene content of 61-66%; HBC 472, a neomexicanus aroma hop with notes of coconut and bourbon; and HBC 682, a superalpha at 18-21%. Whether they ever have names instead of just numbers is very much up to you.

Horizon: high-alpha dual-purpose hopbred in Oregon in 1970; diploid half-sister to Nugget.
Character: floral, citrus.
Alpha 8.8-16.5%, beta 5.5-8.5%, cohumulone 16-22%.
Total oil 0.5-2ml. Myrcene 45-70%, humulene 8-20%, caryophyllene 8-14%, farnesene 3-5%.
Substitutes: Magnum.

Ivanhoe: *see* Cluster.

Jarrylo: new dual-purpose hedgerow hop named after a Slavic fertility god and stablemate of Pekko, Azacca and Summit. Complex fruity aroma profile makes it suitable for single-varietal use in English and Belgian-style ales or as a partner with zippier strains such as Citra.
Character: a fruitbowl including banana, pear and orange, with grassy and spicy notes.
Alpha 15-17%, beta 6-7.5%, cohumulone 34-37%.
Total oil 3.6-4.3ml. Myrcene 40-55%, humulene 15-18%, caryophyllene 8-11%, farnesene <1%.

Legacy: long-established Pacific Northwest dual-purpose variety, but only recently released for sale. Bursting with rich fruit that complements full-bodied stouts and winter ales and also enhances the character of oud bruins and other sour beers.
Character: blackberry, blackcurrant, orange and grapefruit as well as floral and spicy notes.
Alpha 7.8-8.4%.
Substitutes: Cluster, Galena, Northern Brewer.

Lemondrop: powerful aroma variety from Hopsteiner bred from Cascade and a USDA male. Released 2012 to universal acclaim for its rare 'true lemon' aroma, especially evident when used as a very late addition or dry hop.
Character: lemon, mint, green tea, hint of melon.
Alpha 5-7%, beta 4-6%, cohumulone 28-24%.
Total oil 1.5-2ml, farnesene 6-7%.
Substitutes: Cascade, Centennial, Mandarina Bavaria.

Liberty: aroma hop bred in 1983 from Hallertauer Mittelfrüh and a disease-resistant German male; half-sister to Crystal, Ultra and Mount Hood. Low alpha suits it particularly to lagers and light beers.
Character: noble; spicy and resinous.
Alpha 3-6%, beta 3.5%, cohumulone 24-28%.
Total oil 1.3ml. Myrcene 46%, humulene 31%, caryophyllene 9-12%, farnesene <1%.
Substitutes: Hallertauer Mittelfrüh & Tradition, Mount Hood.

Loral: brand-new versatile aroma variety from the Hop Breeding Company, released 2016.
Character: floral, lemon-citrus, pepper, dark fruits.
Alpha 11.3-12.2%, beta 4.9-5.3%, cohumulone 21-24%.
Total oils 1.8-2.9ml. Myrcene 52-58%, humulene 17.8%, caryophyllene 5-5.7%, farnesene 1%, linalool 1-1.1%, B-pinene 0.6-0.7%, geraniol 0.2-0.3%.

Medusa aka Multihead: characterful and distinctive dual-purpose neomexicanus named for its tendency to produce twin cones.
Character: heady floral aroma packed with sweet fruits including guava, apricot and melon.
Alpha 3.5-5.5%, beta 5.5-8%, cohumulone 45%.
Total oil 0.5-1.5ml. Myrcene 48.8%.

Meridian: aroma variety discovered by chance by Oregon State University researchers who at first thought they had a specimen of Willamette's near-obsolete sibling Columbia. As well as its own bright and characterful range of flavours and aromas, Meridian is becoming a highly prized blending hop that both complements and enhances the characters of

such pairings as Citra, Centennial and Glacier.
Character: sweet lemon, orange, tropical fruits, berries.
Alpha 6-7%, beta 6-9%, cohumulone 45%.
Total oil 1-1.4ml.
Substitutes: Citra, Centennial, Glacier.

Millennium: a product of the John I Haas Breeding
Programme, Millennium was, unsurprisingly, released in
the year 2000. A bittering variety directly descended from
Nugget and similar to Columbus, it was bred for disease
resistance and storage stability. Successful in Ameri-
can-style ales and stouts.
Character: mild, herbal, resinous.
Alpha 14.5-16.5%, beta 4.3-5.3%, cohumulone 28-32%.
Total oil 1.8-2.2ml. Myrcene 30-40%, humulene 23-27%,
caryophyllene 9-12%, farnesene <1%.
Substitutes: Columbus, Nugget, Summit, CTZ.

Monroe: brand-new aroma variety from Barth Haas group,
still in its trialling stage at time of writing. Bred from a wild
US variety. Deceptively low acid and oil content.
Character: raspberry and orange syrup aromas; smooth
cherry flavour.
Alpha 2.5%.
Total oil 0.9ml.

Mosaic: high-alpha single-variety hop bred from Simcoe
and Nugget, released 2012. Complex fruity profile has
earned it the nickname 'Citra on steroids'.
Character: mango, pine, tangerine citrus, herbs; tropical
and stone fruit, blueberry, floral and earthy aromas.
Alpha 11.5-13.5%, beta 3.2-3.9%, cohumulone 24-26%.
Total oil 1-1.5ml. Myrcene 47-53%, humulene 13-16%,

caryophyllene 5-8%.
Substitute: Citra.

Mount Hood: aroma variety hugely popular with craft brewers since its release in 1989, Mount Hood is a descendant of Hallertauer Mittelfrüh and is also half-sister to Crystal, Ultra and Liberty.
Character: very subtle noble hop aroma.
Alpha 4-8%, beta 5-8%, cohumulone 21-23%.
Total oil 1-1.7ml. Myrcene 30-40%, humulene 12-38%, caryophyllene 7-16%,farnesene <1%.
Substitutes: Crystal, Strisselspalt, Hersbrucker, Liberty, Hallertauer Mittelfrüh.

Mount Rainier: dual-purpose variety with Magnum, Galena and Fuggle in its ancestry among many others.
Character: Hallertau-like aroma, notes of citrus and liquorice.
Alpha 5-8.1%, beta 5-7%, cohumulone 21-24%.
Total oil 1.5-2.5ml. Myrcene 50-60%, humulene 15-20%, caryophyllene 6-10%, farnesene <1%.
Substitutes: Hallertau, Fuggle.

Neo1: dual-purpose neomexicanus and sibling to Amallia, Neo1 flourishes in the maximum sunlight of its native state. Also naturally pest-resistant due to its abundance of limonene and linalool.
Character: very lemony.
Alpha 7-9%, beta 3-3.3%.

Newport: the hop that saved the West – well, the Northwest, anyway – Newport is the offspring of Magnum and a USDA male variety bred in 2002 to succeed a number of

North-Western bittering varieties threatened by mildew, and thus rescue the region's growers.
Character: clean bitterness, balsamic and vinous flavours.
Alpha 13.5-17%, beta 7.2-9.1%, cohumulone 36-38%.
Total oil 1.6-3.6ml. Myrcene 47-54%, humulene 9%, caryophyllene 1-7%, farnesene <1%.
Substitutes: Galena, Nugget.

Northern Brewer (US): a cross between Northern Brewer and a native variety to suit US growing conditions.
Character: clean, herbal, woody flavours; minty and peppery aroma.
Alpha 8-10%, beta 3.5-5.5%, cohumulone 30-34%.
Total oil 1.2-2ml. Myrcene 35-45%, humulene 20-30%, caryophyllene 10-15%, farnesene 0-1%, B-Pinene 0.4-0.8%; linalool 0.4-0.8%..
Substitute: Chinook.

Nugget: Daughter of Brewer's Gold and mother of Millennium, Nugget's popularity grew quickly after its 1983 release. Only four years later it was producing 14 per cent of the Pacific Northwest's hops. The secret is its balance: an acid profile of high alpha, low beta and low cohumulone produces the bitterness required in IPAs and other hoppy ales, but there's also a high myrcene content.
Character: floral and resinous flavours, herbal aroma.
Alpha 9.5-14%, beta 4.2-5.8%, cohumulone 22-30%.
Total oil 1.5-3ml. Myrcene 48-59%, humulene 12-22%, caryophyllene 7-10%, farnesene 0-1%.
Substitutes: Galena, Olympic.

Olympic: mainly descended from Brewer's Gold but with five other varieties in its lineage including Fuggle and East

H
O
P
S

Kent Golding, Olympic dates back to the 1980s and was a very popular dual-purpose variety immediately on its launch. Despite this, acreage has declined over the years.
Character: notes of spice and citrus.
Alpha 10.6-13.8%, beta 3.8-6.1%, cohumulone 31%.
Total oil 0.86-2.55ml. Myrcene 40.8%, humulene 12.2%, caryophyllene 12%, farnesene 0.9%.
Substitutes: Chinook, Galena, Nugget.

Otto Supreme: very new experimental aroma variety from Yakima Valley Hops, demonstrating perhaps that softer fruit flavour and aroma profiles are beginning to challenge the dominance of very citrous ones.
Character: peach/apricot stone fruit, orange citrus, tropical pineapple and guava.
Alpha 14.6%, beta 9.3%.

Palisade: late hop from Yakima Chief Ranches known for its amazing yield and unique aroma, bred by open pollination of Swiss Tettnanger.
Character: flavours of apricot and citrus; complex flowery, herbal and grassy aromas.
Alpha 5.5-9.5%, beta 6-8%, cohumulone 24-29%.
Total oil 1.4-1.6ml. Myrcene 9-10%, humulene 19-22%, caryophyllene 16-18%, farnesene <1%.
Substitutes: Styrian Golding, Willamette, Glacier, Chinook.

Pekko: new aroma hedgerow variety named after a Finnish farming deity and from the same stable as Azacca, Jarrylo and Summit.
Character: incredibly complex, dominated by herbal and spicy aromas including sage, mint and juniper; floral and fruity notes including melon, pineapple, pear and lemon.

Alpha 13-16%, beta 3-4.25%, cohumulone 27-30%.
Total oil 2.1-2.7ml. Myrecene 46-55%, humulene 12-15%,
caryophyllene 11-13%, farnesene <1%.

Pocket Talisman: *see* Talisman.

Relax: There's no confusion as to whether Relax is an aroma
or a bittering variety – it has almost no alpha acids at all! It
was in fact specifically developed to be an aromatic tisane,
not for brewing use at all but it has been found to work well
in partnership with more conventional varieties.
Character: very aromatic, with lemon and hibiscus alongside celery and green tea.
Alpha 0.25%, beta 13.2%.
Total oil 1.15ml.

San Juan Ruby Red: very little data is available on this new
aroma variety, which was developed by San Juan Hop
Farms in Colorado after being found growing wild in the
mountains. The farm itself appears to have been sold twice
since the variety was tested in 2009, which may be the
source of the difficulty in obtaining details about it.
Character: sweet, fruity, noble.
Alpha 7%.

Santiam: very flowery aroma hop from Oregon released
1997 and descended from Swiss Tettnanger, Hallertauer
Mittelfrüh and Cascade. Often used to enhance the aroma
of IPAs.
Character: soft, herbal, floral and fruity aromas with hints
of pepper and spice.
Alpha 5-8%, beta 5.3-8.5%, cohumulone 18-24%.
Total oil 1.3-1.7ml. Myrcene 25-36%, humulene 23-26%,

caryophyllene 4.8-8.8%, farnesene 8-16%.
Substitutes: Tettnanger, Spalter, Spalter Select, Hallertauer Mittelfrüh, Liberty.

Satus: high alpha dual-purpose hop from Yakima Chief Ranches; well regarded but not a commercial success.
Character: punchy citrus.
Alpha 12.5-14%, beta 8.5-9%, cohumulone 32-35%.
Total oil 1.5-2.8ml. Myrcene 40-45%, humulene 15-20%, caryophyllene 7-10%, farnesene 0-1%.
Substitutes: Nugget, Galena.

Simcoe: Yakima Chief Ranches aroma variety celebrated for its versatility and complexity, released 2000. High alpha and low cohumulone also make it a good bittering hop. Hugely popular with craft and home brewers.
Character: bright citrus flavours with earthy undertones, aromas of passion fruit, grapefruit, pine and herbs.
Alpha 12-14%, beta 4-5%, cohumulone 15-20%.
Total oil 2-2.5ml. Myrcene 60-65%, humulene 10-15%, caryophyllene 5-8%, farnesene 0-1%.

Sonnet: aroma hop independently bred in Oregon from Saaz and Styrian Golding.
Character: floral, grassy, earthy aromas; flavours of oak/honey.
Alpha 2.6-6%.
Substitutes: Saaz, East Kent Goldings, Crystal, Strisselspalt, Hersbrucker.

Sterling: dual-purpose Oregon hop bred from Saaz, Cascade, Early Green and Brewer's Gold; released 1998. Unusual oil composition with very high farnesene and very low caryophyllene.

Character: delicate spicy and citrus aroma with floral and herbal notes.
Alpha 4.5-9%, beta 4-6%, cohumulone 21-28%.
Total oil 0.6-1.9ml. Myrcene 44-48%, humulene 19-23%, caryophyllene 5-8%, farnesene 11-17%.
Substitutes: Saaz, Mount Hood.

Summit: bittering hop bred in Washington State from Nugget, Zeus and Lexus (an unpatented variety). Especially suited to stouts and barley wines.
Character: tangerine, grapefruit and orange aromas.
Alpha 17-19%, beta 4-6%, cohumulone 26-33%.
Total oil 1.5-3ml. Myrcene 30-50%, humulene 15-25%, caryophyllene 10-16%, farnesene <1%.
Substitutes: Columbus, Simcoe, Apollo.

Sun: new bittering hop derived from Brewer's Gold and sister to Zeus, Columbus and Tomahawk.
Character: grassy, herbal.
Alpha 12-16%, beta 4.5-7%, cohumulone 30-40%.
Total oil 2.4-4.5ml. Myrcene 55-70%, humulene 10-15%, caryophyllene 5-10%, farnesene <1%.
Substitutes: Magnum, Galena, Zeus.

Sunbeam: Saaz offspring developed in Oregon as an ornamental variety, but discovered to have good aroma potential.
Character: like Saaz: herbal, earthy, cinnamon-spicy.
Alpha 4-5%, beta 2.5%, cohumulone 36%.
Total oil 0.8-1.3ml. Myrcene 56%, humulene 14%, caryophyllene 4%, farnesene 6%.
Substitutes: Saaz.

Super Galena: super high-alpha Galena–Nugget cross, released 2006. Also noted for relatively high contents of beta acids and myrcene.
Character: clean bittering with mildly fruity aroma. Very like its namesake.
Alpha 13-16%, beta 8-10%, cohumulone 24-20%.
Total oil 1.5-2.5ml. Myrcene 45-60%, humulene 19-24%, caryophyllene 6-14%, farnesene <1%.
Substitutes: Galena.

TNT: proprietary high-alpha blend from Barth Haas that promises an 'explosion' of flavour.
Character: sweet fruits, citrus, herbal.
Alpha 8.8%.
Total oil 0.7ml.

Tahoma: US aroma hop released 2013, high-alpha but low-cohumulone daughter of Glacier. Unusual oil balance.
Character: soft, round, green and woody flavours; high myrcene content creates delicate lemon, orange nose.
Alpha 7.2-8.2%, beta 8.5-9.5%, cohumulone 15-17%.
Total oil 1.5-2ml. Myrcene 67-72%, humulene 9-11%, caryophyllene 2.9-3.5%, farnesene <1%.

Talisman: dual-purpose Cluster variety released in 1965 and very widely grown for its first 10 years until the American taste for much more aromatic beers saw it decline to the point where it is no longer grown for commercial use. A hedgerow version with much the same acid and oil profiles. Pocket Talisman also failed to establish itself in the market.
Alpha 5.7-6.7%, beta 2.8-3.6%, cohumulone 53%.
Total oil 0.72ml. Myrcene 68%, humulene 4%, caryophyllene 5.9%, farnesene 0.2%.

Teamaker: developed over several decades as an ultra-low alpha but high beta aroma hop with no discernible bitterness, Teamaker has perhaps inadvertently become living proof of how versatile the hop's antibacterial properties can be. With the barrier of bitterness removed, Teamaker (as its name suggests!) makes herbal tea that is both tasty and effective against colds and throat infections; it is a natural alternative to antibiotics in livestock feed; and with its bitter taste neutralised it can act as a bacterial inhibitor in food processing. It also has a high concentration of oils, especially myrcene, producing strong and characterful aromas, although the exact composition of oils has not been published.

Character: no bitterness at all; intense earthy, grassy, floral aromas.

Alpha 0.6-1.8%, beta 5.4-13.2%.

Total oil 0.98ml.

Substitutes: Crystal.

Tettnanger (US): dual-purpose hop cloned from Swiss Tettnanger, which is in fact a Fuggle hybrid and not a Tettnanger at all.

Character: noble with spice.

Alpha 4-5%, beta 3-4.5%, cohumulone 20-25%.

Total oil 0.4-0.8ml. Myrcene 30-45%, humulene 18-23%, caryophyllene 6-7%, farnesene 5-8%.

Substitutes: Spalter Select, Santiam, Saaz, Spalter.

Tillicum: high-alpha variety, but with a very high content of beta acids as well. Developed through the John I Haas Inc breeding programme and released in 1995. It is a daughter of Galena and a full sister to Chelan.

Character: stone fruit and citrus.

Alpha 13.5-15.5%, beta 9.5-11.5%, cohumulone 35%.
Total oil 1.5ml. Myrcene 40%, humulene 14%.
Substitutes: Galena, Chelan.

Triple Pearl: aroma hop released 2013, descended from
Perle, Northern Brewer and Hallertau.
Character: subtle aromas of melon, orange, resins, spice
and pepper.
Alpha 10.3-11.2%, beta 3.3-4.4%.
Total oils 1.1-1.8ml. Humulene 7-11%, caryophyllene 3-5%.

Vanguard: aroma hop released 1997, and the last of the
Hallertauer-derived varieties to come from the USDA's
breeding programme. Vanguard possesses a rare balance of
low alpha acids, high beta and low cohumulone, and an oil
composition featuring high levels of humulene.
Character: woody, herbal, sweet, slightly spicy.
Alpha 4.4-6%, beta 6-7%, cohumulone 14-16%.
Total oil 0.9-1.2ml. Myrcene 20-25%, humulene 45-50%,
caryophyllene 12-14%, farnesene 0-1%.
Substitutes: Liberty, Mount Hood, Hallertauer Mittelfrüh,
Saaz.

Vinnie Special: experimental high-alpha variety privately
bred in the Yakima Valley.
Character: mangosteen, pine, coriander.
Alpha 12%, beta 4.8%.

Warrior: proprietary bittering hop much used by US craft
brewers, especially in IPAs, for its mild bittering and zesty
aroma.
Character: citrus and spice aromas.
Alpha 14.5-18%, beta 4.3-6%, cohumulone 22-28%.

Total oil 1-2.5ml. Myrcene 40-50%, humulene 15-20%, caryophyllene 8-11%, farnesene <1%.
Substitutes: Nugget, Columbus.

Willamette: aroma hop descended from Fuggle and released in 1971, Willamette has become a mainstay of the US hop industry and a huge favourite with craft brewers. One of the country's most widely planted varieties, accounting for 20 per cent of US hop acreage; also grown in Australia.
Character: complex spiciness with herbal, floral and fruity notes.
Alpha 4-6%, beta 3-4%, cohumulone 30-35%.
Total oil 1-1.5ml. Myrcene 30-55%, humulene 20-30%, caryophyllene 7-8%, farnesene 5-6%.
Substitutes: Fuggle, Styrian Golding, Tettnanger (US), Glacier, Savinjski Golding.

Willow Creek: neomexicanus from Colorado currently in production trials.

Yakima Gold aka Yakima Goldings: dual-purpose hop developed by Washington State University, released 2013.
Character: grapefruit, lemongrass, lemon zest, spice.
Alpha 8.8-10.5%, beta 4.3-5%, cohumulone 21-23%.
Total oil 1.9-2.3ml. Myrcene 45-50%, humulene 21-25%, caryophyllene 6-8%, farnesene 9-10%.

Yellow Sub: very fruity Barth Haas 'composition' or blend.
Character: sweet apricot, orange citrus, red berries, blackcurrant.
Alpha 6%.
Total oil 1.05ml.

Zeus: aromatic high-alpha hop often classed with Columbus and Tomahawk as CTZ hops.
Character: sweet citrus, herbal aromas.
Alpha 13-17.5%, beta 4-6.5%, cohumulone 26-40%.
Total oil 2.4-4.5ml. Myrcene 45-55%, humulene 9-14%, caryophyllene 5-10%, farnesene <1%.
Substitutes: Columbus/Tomahawk.

Zythos: a blend of American hops specifically designed by Hop Union for American Pale Ales and India Pale Ales. Reportedly a blend of Simcoe, Citra, Palisade and Amarillo, it has distinct tropical (pineapple) and citrus tones, with slight pine characteristics. High alpha content means it can be useful for bittering, but is largely intended to shine as an aroma hop.
Character: tangerine, grapefruit, pine, and pineapple notes.
Alpha 10-12.5%, beta 4.7-6.2%, cohumulone 28%-31%.
Total oil 0.7-1.2ml.
Substitutes: Simcoe, Amarillo.

Poland

Iunga: new hop from IUNG institute at Puławy, developed from Northern Brewer and Marynka. Originally a bittering hop, but richly aromatic as well.
Character: grapefruit, blackcurrant, spice, Black Forest gateau.
Alpha 10-13%, beta 5-8%, cohumulone 29-34%.
Total oil 2-2.6ml. Myrcene 28-33%, humulene 30-40%, caryophyllene 8-11%, farnesene <1%.
Substitutes: Nugget, Target, Galena.

Izabella: dual-purpose hop registered in 1988, a daughter of Lublin and a Styrian male. Production ceased after 2002

but a few plants were found being grown privately and in 2015 the variety was resuscitated. Noteworthy for its unusually high limonene content.
Alpha 6.5-8.5%.

Limbus: hedgerow aroma hop released 1996, bred from Northern Brewer.
Character: intense, more resinous than floral.
Alpha 3-5.5%, beta 2.5-3.5%.
Total oil 1.1-1.5%. Myrcene 30-40%.

Lomik: aroma variety released 1988, a daughter of Northern Brewer.
Character: mild, herbal, spicy.
Alpha 4-5%, beta 2.5-5%, cohumulone 24-28%.
Total oil 0.6-1.2ml. Myrcene 30-45%, humulene 26-29%, caryophyllene 6-10%.
Substitutes: Saaz.

Lubelska aka Lublin, Lubelski: aroma hop ultimately of Czech origin, thought to be a landrace cultivar of Saaz. It has an unusually high humulene and farnesene content.
Character: noble, but with strong aromas of magnolia and lavender as well as mild woody and spicy notes.
Alpha 3-5%, beta 2.5%-4%, cohumulone 25-28%.
Total oils 0.5-1.2ml. Myrcene 22.35%, humulene 30-40%, caryophyllene 6-11%, farnesene <1%, geraniol 0.2-0.3%.
Substitutes: Saaz, Sterling.

Lubelska-Puławy: aroma variety developed from the Lubelska in the 1960s to enhance its bittering quality.
Character: mild European aroma.
Alpha 5-7%, beta 3-5%, cohumulone 23-25%.

Total oil 0.88ml. Myrcene 52%, humulene 14%, caryophyllene 4-6%, farnesene 12%.
Substitutes: Brewer's Gold, Nugget, Glacier.

Magnat: new bittering hop developed from Magnum, released 2012. Very high alpha.
Alpha 11-16%, beta 3-7%.
Total oil 1-2ml. Myrcene 30-40%.

Marynka: developed from Brewer's Gold and released in 1988, Marynka is a dual-purpose variety with pronounced and unusual dark flavours and aromas.
Character: intense earthy, floral and herbal aroma, including liquorice.
Alpha 9-12%, beta 10.2-13%, cohumulone 26-33%.
Total oil 1.8-2.2ml. Myrcene 28-31%, humulene 36-33%, caryophyllene 10-13%, farnesene 1.8-2.2%.
Substitutes: Tettnanger.

Nadwyslanka: aroma hop developed in 1976 from an old Polish variety; poor vigour and yield mean it is no longer grown commercially.
Character: noble aroma.
Alpha 6%, beta 3.2%, cohumulone 23%.
Total oil 0.5ml. Myrcene 32%, humulene 27%, caryophyllene 8.2%, farnesene 13.5%.

Oktawia: bittering hop released in 1996, a hybridisation of Brewer's Gold and Northern Brewer. Note the humulene.
Character: deep, floral, resinous.
Alpha 7-9%, beta 3-4.5%, cohumulone 33-37%.
Total oil 0.7-1.4ml. Myrcene 30-50%, humulene 36-40%, caryophyllene 6-8%, farnesene <1%.

Pulawski: bittering variety descended from Lubelski, released 2012.
Character: spicy, fruit.
Alpha 8.2%, beta 3.6%.
Total oil 1.7ml.

Sybilla: new bittering variety from IUNG at Puławy, a cross of Lublin and Styrian Golding. High humulene and farnesene create interesting aromas to complement its bittering qualities.
Character: intense lemon, pine and floral aromas.
Alpha 6-8%, beta 4-7%, cohumulone 9-11%.
Total oil 1.5-2.2ml. Myrcene 28-30%,humulene 40-45%, caryophyllene 9-11%, farnesene 6-9%.
Substitutes: Perle, Hallertau, Fuggle, Sterling, Cascade.

Tomyski: traditional aroma hop grown in Western Poland since the 1830s, originally a cross of Bavarian and Bohemian varieties. The region's hop yards were virtually destroyed by the Germans during World War II, but the old Tomyski is still being grown.
Character: noble.
Alpha 2.5-4%, beta 4-7%, cohumulone 26%.
Total oil 0.8-1.2ml. Myrcene 15%, humulene 45%.

Zbyszko: intense hedgerow bittering variety released in 1996, a cross of Lubelski and Brewer's Gold.
Character: very intense, sharp, even harsh resinous aroma.
Alpha 5-8%, beta 5.7-7%.
Total oil 1-1.5ml. Myrcene 30-40%.

Zula: bittering hop released 2004, a cross of Lubelski and Styrian Golding.

Alpha 10-14%, beta 5-7%.
Total oil 1-1.2ml. Myrcene 30-40%.

Slovenia & The Balkans

Ahil: introduced 1972; a 'Super Styrian' with both high alpha and high aroma levels. A cross between Brewer's Gold and a wild male. Never really challenged the popularity of the more established Styrian and Savinjski Golding, and is no longer widely grown.
Alpha 10-12%, beta 4-5%, cohumulone 25%.
Total oil 1.8-2.2ml. Myrcene 61.1%, humulene 7.6%, caryophyllene 4.3%, farnesene 10.4%.

Apolon: originally a bittering hop but now considered dual-purpose. Introduced as a Super Styrian in the 1970s and since reclassified as a Slovenian hybrid, it's a cross between Brewer's Gold and a Yugoslavian wild male and is a sibling of Aurora, Ahil and Atlas. Now hard to obtain.
Alpha 10-12%, beta 4%, cohumulone 2.25%.
Total oil 1.3-1.6ml. Myrcene 63%, humulene 26%, caryophyllene 4%, farnesene 11.3%.

Ardeal: highly resistant large-cone superalpha from Romania, a clone of Hallertau Magnum developed at the Hops & Medicinal Plants Crop Research Centre in Cluj and originally called Cluj Superalfa.
Alpha 13.8-14.5%.

Aroma: high-yielding Serbian aroma variety.

Atlas aka Styrian Atylas: aroma hop released in the 1970s, Atlas also has good bittering qualities. As with its siblings, though, production has been cut back following its

incorrect classification as a Super Styrian. It's actually a seedling of Brewer's Gold, and typically used to add a rich aroma to light-bodied ales.
Character: intense notes of lime, blossom and pine.
Alpha 9-11%, beta 4%, cohumulone 36%.
Total oil 1.3-1.6ml. Myrcene 59%, humulene 9%, caryophyllene 4%, farnesene 13.3%.
Substitutes: Aurora, Styrian Golding.

Aurora aka Super Styrian: a seedling of Northern Brewer, Aurora is a dual-purpose strain with a distinctive aroma arising from its balance of essential oils, and nearly twice the alpha content of Styrian Golding.
Character: earthy, spicy, herbal.
Alpha 7-12%, beta 2.7-5%, cohumulone 22-26%.
Total oil 0.9-1.8ml. Myrcene 51%, humulene 17-25%, caryophyllene 5-9%, farnesene 5-10%.
Substitutes: Styrian Golding, Northern Brewer.

Backa: dating to 1956, Backa is a now rare Serbian aroma variety of unknown pedigree. It suffered from poor yields and declining alpha levels.
Character: said to have noble qualities.
Alpha 4.8%, beta 25%, cohumulone 25%.
Total oil 0.6ml. Humulene 33%.

Blisk: aroma hop of the same generation as Bobek and Buket, never taken up by commercial growers.
Alpha 9.5-14.1%, beta 3.3-4.8%, cohumulone 33%.
Total oil 1.24-3.24ml. Humulene 11.5%.

Bobek: dual-purpose cross between Northern Brewer and a Slovenian male, bred to combine intense bittering with luscious aromas and flavours. Much more successful than its stablemates Blisk and Buket, and now one of the country's most widely planted varieties.

Character: floral, lemon, pine.

Alpha 3.5-7%, beta 4-6%, cohumulone 27-31%.

Total oil 0.7-4ml. Myrcene 30-45%, humulene 13-19%, caryollyphene 4-6%, farnesene 3-7%.

Substitutes: Fuggle, Willamette, Styrian Golding.

Buket: dual-purpose variety bred from Fuggle and Northern Brewer in the 1970s, part of the same high alpha-high aroma programme as Bobek and Blisk. Not a commercial success.

Alpha 11%, beta 4.9%, cohumulone 24%.

Total oil 2.15ml. Myrcene 57%, humulene 17%, caryophyllene 5.4%, farnesene 5.5%.

Cekin: aroma hop selected at the Hop Research Institute, Žatec, in the 1980s, sibling of Cicero. An intensely aromatic cross between Aurora and a local male; distinctive, but not a commercial success outside its native country.

Character: earthy and mild, similar to Styrian hops.

Alpha 6-8%, beta 2-3%, cohumulone 24%.

Total oil 1.07ml. Myrcene 47.9%, humulene 16.5%, caryophyllene 7.2%, farnesene 7.1%.

Substitutes: Celeia, Cicero.

Celeia: extremely successful triploid hybrid of Aurora, Styrian Golding and a native wilding; sibling of Cerera. A versatile aroma hop, much used in lighter-bodied beers, and today the most widely planted variety in Slovenia.

Character: earthy, herbal, floral and citrus aroma.

Alpha 3-6%, beta 2.3-4%, cohumulone 23-29%.

Total oil 1.31ml. Myrcene 49.5%, humulene 17.6%, caryophyllene 8-9%, farnesene 5.6%.
Substitutes: Saaz, Bobek, Styrian Golding.

Cerera: Celeia's sister, similar to Saaz. Developed in the1980s from Savinjski Golding and a Yugoslav male and classified as a seedless Super Styrian triploid. High in tannins and therefore best used in combination with other high alpha varieties.
Character:mild Saaz-like aroma.
Alpha 5-6%, beta 4-4.5%, cohumulone 25%.
Total oil 1.5ml. Myrcene 58%, humulene 13.2%, caryophyllene 6%, farnesene 3%.

Cicero: sister to Cekin, Cicero is a dual-purpose hop bred from Aurora, a Yugoslav tetraploid male and a USDA tetraploid male in the 1980s.
Character: moderate bittering; lightly spicy, floral.
Alpha 6-7%, beta 2.4%, cohumulone 29%.
Total oil 1.05ml. Myrcene 51%, humulene 18%, caryophyllene 9-11%, farnesene 3%.
Substitutes: Aurora, Cekin, Celeia.

Dana aka Extra Styrian Dana: dual-purpose hop bred from Hallertau Magnum and a wild Slovenian male; mostly selected for its aromas. Characterful dry hop.
Character: subtle floral and citrus flavours
Alpha 11-16%, beta 4-6%, cohumulone 28-31%.
Total oil 2.4-3.9ml. Myrcene 50-59%, humulene 15-21.6%, caryophyllene 5.7-7.6%, farnesene 6.9-8.7%.
Substitutes: Celeia, Bobek.

Dunav: a triploid cross of Northern Brewer, Styrian Golding

and a wild male, Dunav was bred in the 1960s to succeed the low-yielding Backa as an aroma variety. However, it never caught on commercially and remains in limited production in Serbia. Sibling to Neoplanta and Vojvodina.
Character: mild noble aroma.
Alpha 5.1-9.6%, beta 2.8-4.6%, cohumulone 30%.
Total oil 1.19ml. Myrcene 19%, humulene 19%, caryophyllene 6%, farnesene 6.2%.

Neoplanta: dual-purpose offspring of Northern Brewer, Savinjski Golding and a wild Slovenian male, bred in the 1960s at the same time as Vojvodina and Dunav to succeed low-yielding landrace variety Backa.
Alpha 7-12%, beta 2.9-5%, cohumulone 36%.
Total oil 1.3ml. Myrcene 49%, humulene 20%, caryophyllene 8.9%, farnesene 5%.

Robusta: high-yielding Serbian aroma variety.

Savinjski Golding: *see* Styrian Golding.

Styrian Cardinal: astonishingly complex and versatile new aroma hop from the Institute for Hop Research whose high myrcene level is causing quite a stir with home and craft brewers.
Character: aromas and flavours of rich fruits (pineapple, plum, banana, blackcurrant), citrus (orange, lime, lemongrass), herbs (marjoram) and spices (curry-leaf, ginger) as well as caramel, menthol, hay and geranium.
Alpha 10-15%, beta 3.2-4.6%, cohumulone 31-37%.
Total oil 1.8-2.7ml. Myrcene 40-50%, humulene 15-22%, caryophyllene 8-11%, farnesene 5-7%.
Styrian Gold: not to be confused with Styrian Golding

(actually a Fuggle), Styrian Gold is a dual-purpose variety bred from Savinjski Golding and a Slovenian wild male and released in 2009.

Character: balanced noble aroma with unusual notes of honey, oregano, basil, nettle and hay.

Alpha 3.5-6.5%, beta 3.5-5.9%, cohumulone 28-35%.

Total oil 1.3-2.3ml. Myrcene 38-47%, humulene 19-22%, caryophyllene 5-10%, farnesene 6-10%.

Substitutes: Styrian Golding.

Styrian Golding aka Savinjski Golding: aroma hop in worldwide demand; famously not a Golding at all, but (according to tradition) a clonal selection of Fuggle that dates to the 1930s and has earned its longevity through resistance to disease.

Character: resinous, earthy, peppery.

Alpha 2.8-6%, beta 2-3%, cohumulone 25-30%.

Total oil 0.3-1ml. Myrcene 27-33%, humulene 34-38%, caryophyllene 9-11%, farnesene 2%-5%.

Substitutes: Summit, Fuggle, Willamette, Bobek, East Kent Golding.

Styrian Wolf: expect intense and concentrated fruit flavours from this second Institute of Hop Research new release, which has a very high myrcene content.

Character: tropical fruits including passion fruit, banana, mango and melon; hot spices; the entire spectrum of citrus flavours; herby and floral geranium, parsley, thyme, hay and anise.

Alpha 13.5-18.5%, beta 5-6%, cohumulone 22-23%.

Total oil 2.2-3.6ml. Myrcene 60-70%, humulone 5-9%, caryophyllene 2-3%, farnesene 4.5-6.5%.

Vojvodina: dual-purpose cross between Northern Brewer

and Savinjski Golding, Vojvodina was created in the 1960s at the former Yugoslavia's Institute for Agricultural Research. The sibling of Neoplanta and Dunav, but not widely regarded as successful and today considered scarce.
Character: woody aroma, cedar, tobacco.
Alpha 6.1-10.5%, beta 2.3-4.7%, cohumulone 30%.
Total oil 0.6-1.4ml. Myrcene 67%, humulene 13%, caryophyllene 5%, farnesene 0.6%.
Substitutes: Northern Brewer, Goldings.

South Africa

Hybrid-2: seedling of California Cluster developed as an aroma variety in South Africa in the 1940s, discontinued due to low yields but still grown in Kashmir.
Alpha 10.2%, beta 6.3%, cohumulone 32%.
Total oil 0.91ml. Myrcene 52%, humulene 3%, caryophyllene 9%, farnesene 3.9%.
Substitutes: Yakima Cluster, California Cluster.

Outeniqua: bittering hop rarely seen outside its native South Africa; mother to the more widely distributed Southern Star. Day-neutral, which means it flourishes well in the shorter daylight hours of sub-tropical South Africa.
Character: light herbal aroma, slightly spicy.
Alpha 12-13.5%, beta 4.1-5.1%, cohumulone 25-30%.
Total oil 1.6ml. Myrcene 38-43%, humulene 28-33%, caryophyllene 9-10%, farnesene 0-1%.
Substitutes: Southern Star.

Southern Brewer: bittering hop developed in the 1970s. Not a great commercial hit and ultimately succeeded by Southern Promise and Outeniqua.
Alpha 5.6-12%, beta 2.8-5%, cohumulone 33-42%.

Total oil 0.4-1.5ml. Myrcene 50-62%, humulene 10-26%, caryophyllene 4-10%, farnesene 3-11.2%.
Substitutes: Southern Promise.

Southern Promise: bittering hop created from Southern Brewer and a wild Slovenian male. Like its contemporary Outeniqua, Southern Promise is a day-neutral variety. Originally intended as dual-purpose, it has fairly high alpha acids and low cohumulone, giving it bright and smooth bittering qualities.
Character: woody, earthy aromas.
Alpha 9.5-11.5%, beta 3.6-5.4%, cohumulone 20-22%. Total oil 0.7-1.1ml. Myrcene 22%, humulene 26%, caryophyllene 9%, farnesene 0-1%.
Substitutes: Southern Brewer.

Southern Star: cross between Outeniqua and a South African male, released in 2001 by African Breweries Hop Farms. One of the highest alpha hops to come from the region and primarily a bittering agent in IPAs, but high oil levels also lend a tangy aroma.
Alpha 12-14%, beta 4.8-5.2%, cohumulone 31%.
Total oil 1.6ml. Myrcene 39%, humulene 22%, caryophyllene 15%, farnesene 12%.
Substitutes: Outeniqua.

Ukraine including Russia

Al'ta: bittering variety originally bred from Saaz.
Alpha 8.8%, beta 4%.
Total oil 1.22ml.

Gaidamatskyi: aroma hop.
Alpha 4.8%, beta 5.6%, cohumulone 28%.

Granite: bittering hop.
Alpha 7.2%, beta 3.3%, cohumulone 16.9%.

Hmeleslav: aroma hop.
Alpha 3.7%, beta 4.1%, cohumulone 22.1%.

Klon-18: high-alpha hop bred in the 1950s from an old Czech variety, Zemsevy. Similar to Saaz and Lublin.

Kumyr: bred from Saaz.
Alpha 7.2%, beta 3.9%, cohumulone 16.7%.

Nasar: bittering hop.
Alpha 7.3%, beta 4.9%, cohumulone 26.4%.

Nasionalnyi: aroma hop.
Alpha 7-9%, beta 5.4%.
Total oil 0.48ml.

Poliskyi: bittering variety.

Promin: new bittering variety bred from Saaz, released 2013.
Alpha 7.5%, beta 4.1%, cohumulone 29%.

Ruslan: dual-purpose variety.
Alpha 6.7%, beta 4.7%, cohumulone 44.1%.

Serebrianka aka Silver: unusual aroma variety from a traditional Russian hop-growing region, Chuvashia. Judging by its aroma profile it was probably originally bred from a noble hop. US trials foundered on its poor growth and lack of resistance, but not before it had parented Cascade. Still available for craft and homebrewing. Very low alpha; high humulene and farnesene.

Character: mild aroma and flavour with hints of black tea, herbs and tobacco.

Alpha 3-4%, beta 3%, cohumulone 23%.

Total oil 0.41ml. Myrcene 30%, humulene 27%, caryophyllene 8%, farnesene 12%.

Substitute: Premiant.

Slavianka: aroma variety.
Alpha 3.8%, beta 5.4%.
Total oil 0.78ml.

Slavonian: aroma hop.
Alpha 4.6%, beta 5.9%, cohumulone 23.3%.

Starovolynskyi Aromatichnyi: aroma variety.

Triumf: aroma variety.

Ukrainskyi Aromatichnyi: aroma hop.

Xanthi: dual-purpose hop.
Alpha 6.2%, beta 4%, cohumulone 35.1%.

Zahrava: new aroma hop, bred from Saaz and released 2013.
Alpha 5.7%, beta 4.7%.
Total oil 0.67ml.

Zlato Polissia: aroma variety.

Zmina: bittering variety.

OTHER FLAVOURINGS

2: Other Flavourings

Historians of beer and brewing have counted nearly 200 plants of one sort or another that have been mentioned as ingredients in historical British and Continental brewing. All of them also had medicinal uses, and it may well be that they were first employed in brewing not to improve the beer, but to act as a solvent for the active parts of the plant. In Northern Europe during the medieval period, brewers bought proprietary compounds of mixed herbs (collectively termed 'gruit' and often a state or church monopoly) to flavour, clear, and preserve their ales and to aid digestion and to treat dietary ailments; and in late medieval and early modern Britain, even after the use of hops had became the norm, brewers in some regions still frequently used aromatic and dietary herbs such as sweet gale, marsh trefoil, heather, ground ivy and herb bennet for those same purposes. It's uncertain how and when all these herbal additions were actually made, since medieval ale wasn't boiled. Sometimes they appear to have been infused in the mash; another practice was to pile the herbs up to form mats through which the mash was sieved; another was to boil the herbs separately to make very concentrated teas that were then strained into the mash (which is how traditional Lithuanian craft brewers still hop their beer today).

Hops, with their charges of acids and antioxidants, may well have been used in cloth production as yellow-brown dyes and dye fixatives well before anyone discovered their preservative and aromatising properties. Their fibres also make strong cord and the young shoots are edible. Their application to brewing, originating as far as we know in 9th-century Germany, probably stems from the practice of infusing the cones to make medicinal tisanes. Over many years they proved commercially superior to herbs and gruit in three very important respects. Their preservative qualities allowed the brewer to make weaker beer that cost less, lasted longer and could be traded more widely. Their aromas and flavours were in almost all cases very much more concentrated than those of the various herbs they replaced.

And as a single vine-grown crop rather than a multitude of shrubs, roots and herbs they also lent themselves more readily to cost-efficient large-scale cultivation, making possible an organised, regular supply well-suited to serving the organised, regular brewing industry operating in the growing cities of Germany, the Low Countries and England.

By the mid-17th century unhopped ale had died out completely as a commercial product, but not its associated herbal lore. Only in the northern extremities of Europe did ancient practices cling on – as they still do in parts of Scandinavia and the Baltic. However, in the towns and cities medicinal beers flavoured with hops – and also laden with herbal sovereigns, specifics and cure-alls – were widely available as proprietary blends concocted by quacks such as James I of England's physician, one Dr (a courtesy title only) Butler. Dr Butler's curative beer was still being sold as late as the mid-18th century. After that, though, brewing with herbs and spices (with a handful of exceptions such as liquorice and ginger) died out, and brewing with fruit was more or less confined to a tiny corner of Belgium.

For the inquisitive and imaginative craft and home brewer of today, though, anything is possible, and many craft breweries in Britain and America are revisiting the ingredients of the past from spruce tips to sweet gale as well as investigating newer ones such as citrus peel, coffee and chocolate. For although the hop is without doubt a wonderful boon, especially given the glorious and growing diversity of modern varieties, the brewer's world today is a world of many flavours.

Below are a few of them for you to experiment with. Various parts of the plant may be used, normally dried. They can be added during the boil and/or fermentation or in lieu of a dry hop; but remember that their essential oil content is likely to be much lower than the hop's. Experiment with tisanes and neutral trial brews before committing to larger gyles.

Warning: Some herbs and spices including nutmeg, liquorice and chilli can have harmful side-effects if used in very large quantities.

OTHER FLAVOURINGS

Alehoof aka Ground Ivy: a chemically rich and naturally abundant creeping shrub (too abundant if it gets into your lawn!) Glechoma hederacea steeped in wine was once considered almost a cure-all and was used to treat gout, sciatica, skin diseases of all sorts, throat infections (as a gargle with honey) and just about any ailments of the respiratory and digestive tracts. For the brewer, its eucalyptol, menthol and pinene content made for a pleasant, fresh, minty flavour and aroma while its triterpenoids, iodine and gleheda (a natural insecticide), generated a protective bitterness. It was also prized as a primitive form of fining: the leaves were dried, crumbled and sprinkled over the surface of the fermented ale whereupon their negatively-charged polysaccharides acted just as Irish moss does, gathering up positively-charged particles and sinking to the bottom of the tun.

Anise: Pimpinella anisum is the most concentrated source of anethole, the essential oil that puts the flavour into aniseed, fennel and liquorice, with a content of up to 7 per cent. It is also the most expensive and hardest to get. Chinese star anise, illicium verum, is actually no relation but carries up to 4 per cent anethole as well as various cinnamon compounds. (Japanese star anise is extremely poisonous and is only used to make incense and perfume.)

Black pepper: increasingly popular as a means of giving a spicy lift to stouts and saisons, Piper nigrum is also mildly antimicrobial and has traditionally been used by herbalists as a topical treatment for minor ailments such as mouth ulcers, sunburn and toothache. Its pungency comes from piperine and rotundone (which is so strong it can be detected at almost homeopathic levels), but the black outer layer also carries pinene, limonene, caryophyllene and linalool. Lightly crushed peppercorns can be added at any point from early in the boil right through to secondary, but go easy at first and choose your aroma hop with care – you want them to complement each other, not fight! Also, don't use pink peppercorns – they're not pepper at all, they're a nut and therefore an allergen.

Bog myrtle aka sweet gale: among the many dozens of shrubs and herbs employed by the brewers of yore, Myrica gale is the beer historian's favourite, partly no doubt because of its slightly rude name. But as a flavouring for ale it was no joke: like sage, it came close to possessing the whole hop package. The parts used are the leaves, seeds and short pieces of stem, which mixed together make a formidable cocktail of preservatives: tannin, the antibacterial myricatin, the insect repellent myrtenol and the insecticide germacrene. But it's also incredibly aromatic, containing our old friends myrcene, caryophyllene, pinene and limonene as well as the incredibly pungent eucalyptol. Highland ghillies say you can smell a clump of the stuff half a mile away. In recent years a number of craft brewers on both sides of the Atlantic have experimented with gale in IPAs, wheat beers and stouts, normally as a judicious addition a few minutes before the end of the boil: the results, they say, are nothing like you'd expect but very pleasant nonetheless.

Chamomile: the dried flowers of Chamaemelum nobile (Roman chamomile) and Matricaria recutita (German chamomile) are sources of the same oils – humulene, caryophyllene and farnesene – that give hops their earthy, spicy and herbal characters. Usually used either to make a soothing lotion to treat chicken-pox and other skin outbreaks or

131

OTHER FLAVOURINGS

as a tisane, the dried flowers can be bought as tea and used at any stage of the brew. Loose-leaf is preferable to bags as it is usually fresher. Chamomile also possesses antibacterial properties and is said to enhance the bubblegum flavour of wheat beers.

Chestnuts: chestnuts can be roasted and ground and used as part of a gluten-free mash, but added at later stages they bring a special silky richness that makes a little effort worthwhile. The trouble is that they take more than a little effort. Peeling, roasting and grinding a worthwhile quantity yourself will take all week. You can buy ready-prepared chestnut chips, but they're expensive. A less laborious way is to make a tincture of toasted (as light or as dark as you like) and coarsely ground nuts in a jam-jar of brandy or dark rum, left for two weeks and regularly shaken, and then add it to the secondary. Or, of course, you can always cheat – an easier way still of achieving the same effect is simply to add tinned chestnut purée to the secondary. Lightly crushed tinned or vacuum-packed marron glacé will also do at a pinch, but remember that they contain extra sugar, so unless you make the necessary adjustments your final alcohol by volume will be slightly higher.

Chilli: many members of the capsicum tribe can be used as a flavour additive to give any beer from Pilsner to porter a dramatic flourish. However, it's a rather one-dimensional ingredient: the effect of the capsaicin grabbing hold of the pain receptors in your mouth will overwhelm anything subtle! Don't use the very hottest types such as Scotch bonnet or habanero – stick with something moderate (especially the everyday jalapeño, which has the additional virtue of being easy to find) and use more of it if you want more heat.

The chilli can be fresh or dried, green or red-ripe, and you can add it a few minutes before flame-out and then let it steep for a few minutes more. Or you can make the addition at the start of primary fermentation and remove the chillies when you rack the beer off into secondary. Alternatively, if you're bottling the beer you can pop a wee pepper into each one. As well as the heat, the pepper should create a background fruitiness; but perhaps its most pleasing effect is that your brain fights back against the pain by releasing a great waft of endorphins.

Chocolate: chocolate stout has become very popular in the last decade or so, but strictly speaking, putting actual chocolate in it is cheating. The chocolate flavour should derive from the blend of malts in your grist – typically chocolate malt (of course!), amber or biscuit malt, and crystal malt or carapils. The various forms of chocolate itself don't actually contribute a great deal to the flavour but do give an earthy depth and rich texture that are worth having. Dark (i.e. unsweetened) cooking chocolate and cacao nibs seem to give the best results, either as melted baking chocolate (double the quantity of cocoa powder is an alternative) added right at the end of the boil, or as nibs (crushed and roasted cacao beans) in the secondary fermentation, or both but in half quantities.

Cinnamon: the rich, luxurious aroma of cinnamon and its sweet, spicy flavour make it one of the most popular spices in the world – indeed, it's almost impossible to get a slice of apple pie that isn't doused in it. And it brews well, too, the high concentration of cinnamaldehyde backed up by trace amounts of eugenol, caryophyllene and linalool giving almost any style of beer a heady waft. Brewers do

OTHER FLAVOURINGS

worry how to add it, though: the aromatics in Cinnamomum verum tend not to survive boiling well. Infusing a few roughly crumbled sticks (in a bag, of course) in the secondary is one way; another is to make a tincture of crumbled sticks in a sealed jar of vodka or white rum, let it steep for a week and then add it at the very end of the secondary or even to the bottling bucket. Goes well with other flavours, especially honey and vanilla, for a pint that's more like a feather bed than a beer.

Citrus peel: citrus flavours and aromas are better intensified by use of the zest – the outer peel without the bitter white pith – than by whole fruit, which can spell death for head retention. And it's surprising how little you need: Curaçao orange peel is one of the key components in the flavour and aroma of wheat beer, but recipes recommend tiny doses of two grams per litre or even less, added 5-10 minutes before the end of the boil (the longer it spends in the boil the less you need, but then the aroma will suffer). Of course Curaçao orange is not the only citrus peel you can add to beer. Lemon is an obvious candidate, but grapefruit is fast catching up in popularity – and imagine an ice-cold grapefruit wheat on a heatstroke afternoon if you want to know why! Satsuma, tangelo, even bergamot have all found their way into pale beers, and Seville orange into dark ones.

We've seen how little goes into wheat beer, and the same holds good for other peels: they can be overwhelming if the dosage is too high. So, 1-2g per litre of fresh zest added 5-10 minutes before the end of the boil, or 15 minutes if your peel is dried, should be quite enough. (It actually does no harm if you dry your own fresh peel in a very low temperature oven, as if you were baking a meringue.

Another small addition in the secondary ferment adds

to the aroma without spoiling the flavour. You could also steep a few grams in a little boiling water to add to your bottling bucket.

Cloves: perhaps the most pungent of all spices thanks to the dominance of eugenol in its chemical make-up along with caryophyllene, vanillin and tannins, the dried bud of Syzygium aromaticum (also known as Caryophyllus aromaticus) really is one-dimensional and also rather over-powering. It can be useful if you're making a wheat beer and either don't have the right yeast or have allowed the fermentation temperature to creep up: a small handful of cloves (no more than one for five litres, really!) will redress the balance. Otherwise generally used in mixtures, especially at Christmas. Either use as a tincture or add (in a bag with other spices) a few minutes before the end of the boil and then steep for an hour.

Coconut: an increasingly popular additive, especially to strong and dark ales, coconut doesn't have an overpowering flavour of its own; but perhaps because of its high oil content it does create a silky-smooth mouthfeel that works particularly well with the darker malts. Most brewers use it chopped and lightly toasted in a very low temperature oven to create the Maillard reaction that seems to enhance its nutty flavour; its high ester and ketone content balance out the toasted meat's caramel sweetness with a sharp, fresh stab. Add after the boil or to primary or secondary – or all three! – using a mesh bag. If toasting coconut, keep a sharp eye on it: it does nothing for ages, then browns suddenly, then burns. Or cheat and use an extract!

Coffee: as with chocolate stout, an expert brewer can use the malt grist alone to create a coffee flavour. And again, the components of the grist are likely to be amber or biscuit malt, crystal malt or carapils, and chocolate malt (but only a very little). But would it really be coffee porter without coffee? Of course it wouldn't! Opt for a medium roast that is neither too harsh nor too bland, and coarse-grind the beans yourself because the coffee shop is likely to reduce them to a powder that will form an unskimmable scum. Make your coffee in a cafetière as normal, or cold-steep the ground beans for 24 hours, then strain off the liquid and add it to the bottling bucket. Alternatively the beans themselves might be added to the boil at the very end, in which case a judicious second addition could be used as a dry-hop or (if bottling) added to the secondary.

Conifer needles: the fresh green tips of most pines, firs and spruces (but not yew, which is highly poisonous) have long been popular flavourings for beer, giving that clean, fresh aroma so beloved of the manufacturers of cleaning products. Most drinkers might find pine beer a little overpowering given the oil's extremely high levels of the very pungent terpinolene as well as linalool, limonene and anethole. Spruce tips are gentler: camphene and pinene dominate, giving a sweeter and more lemony aroma, with myrcene for fruitiness. The word 'spruce' actually means 'from Prussia', and a very dark wild-fermented beer originally brewed in Prussia, flavoured with spruce tips and known as Dantzig (sic) after the port from which it was traded, was a serious style of beer on the English market from the early 15th to the early 20th centuries. Spruce tips were also much used by the first American colonists in place of hops, and it is also said that sea captains on long voyages (including

Captain Cook) used spruce tips when they could get them – and, presumably, other aromatic botanicals – to disguise the disgusting taste of the all-molasses 'beer' they brewed once their regular supplies were exhausted. Use pine needles extremely sparingly late in the boil; you can afford to be a little more generous with spruce tips.

Coriander seed: the subtle and complex aroma of the seed of Coriandrum sativa, with its notes of warm orange and light, clean pepper, is the classic partner to Curaçao orange peel in wheat beers of all sorts. It works just as well by itself to enrich saisons and counterbalance the weight of much stronger beers. The dominant flavour component is the floral and spicy linalool, with geraniol and pinene bringing up the rear. Use cracked, sparingly and in a bag either 10-15 minutes before flameout, with another 10-15 minutes' steeping afterwards, or during secondary.

Earl Grey tea: perhaps the most user-friendly source of that most wonderful of aromatics, bergamot orange oil. Bergamot orange (or just plain bergamot), Citrus bergamia is a hybrid of sweet lime and Seville orange. Its essential oil, squeezed from the peel, is nearly 40 per cent linalool/linalyl acetate and 37 per cent limonene resulting in an astonishingly heady floral and citrus aroma; the 3 per cent pinene thrown in for good measure tops it off with a clean, fresh bounce. The easiest way to use Earl Grey is as a tea, as weak or as strong as you like, added whenever you like; the tannins that come from the tealeaves themselves provides some bittering balance and a bit of protection. Use looseleaf rather than bagged tea: it's fresher.

OTHER FLAVOURINGS

Elderberries: elderberries are very tannic and need a considerable maturing period to mellow. A little goes a long way, too: even quite a small addition can generate a wonderful port-like depth that turns any dark winter ale into the perfect digestif. Some brewers dry the berries slightly in a low temperature oven before use, roll them lightly to break the skins, then use them whole in the boil; others push them (uncooked) through a fine sieve with a wooden spoon, discard the skin, seeds and pulp, and add the juice at primary fermentation.

Elderflowers: to call naturally sparkling elderflower wine 'elderflower champagne' is now a crime for which the French secret service will hunt you down and guillotine you. But elderflower wine is one of the many beverages – like ginger 'beer' and nettle 'beer' – that are really just sugar fermentations made potable by any old aromatic that comes to hand. And as elderflowers are perhaps the most delicious of all easily-available aromatics they are well worth brewing with. There are two methods: either the traditional ginger/nettle beer method but using malt extract instead of sugar; or making a light beer and adding elderflower florets in a muslin bag towards the end of the boil. To separate the florets from the stalks you lay a large clean cloth on the table, take a head of elderflowers in each hand and then rub them vigorously together to create a kind of snowstorm. It's pretty! And pretty tedious, too – if using the former method you need a whole litre of florets for a 5-litre mash. Essences are available if you don't mind being accused of cheating.

Flowers: If a flower smells nice when you pick it, then the chances are that it will still smell nice if you brew with it; and on the basis of that probability adventurous brewers are experimenting with just about anything the park-keeper doesn't see them making off with. Used in fairly neutral light beers some flowers will give predictable results – rosebuds, hibiscus, peach blossom and jasmine, for instance, will remain very much as they are. Some will surprise you – you won't realise how bitter dandelions can be! Some, such as Calendula, so popular as a cosmetic oil, seem promising but can give disappointing results. Make a tisane or a tincture of your chosen flower for test purposes, and do try mixing and matching. Your final selections should be dried in a very, very low oven or they'll hardly keep a few days; if you do need to keep them, pack them tightly into an airtight jar with just enough vodka to cover them. Whole fresh flowers can be added very late in the boil; teas and tinctures can be added to the secondary or at bottling; dried flowers can be used as dry hops. If brewing with foraged flowers, stay well away from all umbellifers, because although angelica is delicious and is commonly found as a botanical in gin, hemlock is deadly, and the chances are that you won't know the difference.

Ginger: of all the dozens and dozens of flavour additives used in brewing, ginger must be one of the most common. Not as in the traditional ginger beer, though: that isn't really beer at all, just syrup with chopped root ginger, lemon peel and yeast. But ginger, Zingiber officinale, is a good ingredient in proper beer as well, whether it's to pep up a light summer beer or to add zing to a strong, dark Christmas beer (along with nutmeg, cinnamon and cloves, of course!). And there are many ways of adding it. Some brewers throw in the chopped root halfway through the boil, which mellows the fieriness but retains all the flavour and aroma. But they use incredible quantities – a kilo to 25 litres in one recipe, 1.5kg in another – whereas the amount you need if you pop it into the secondary instead goes right down to 50g for a pleasantly but not too aggressively gingery summer beer or, at most, 250g for something that you wouldn't want to accompany a hot curry or chilli with! And there's always the cordial alternative: 50-100g to a litre of water, simmered for 45 minutes in a lidded pan to mini-mise evaporation, with 300-400g of sugar to compensate for the dilution of the wort, should do the job nicely.

Hazelnuts: all ale in traditional folk songs is 'nut-brown', which one might suppose to be a polite way of saying 'unappetisingly murky', but many brewers are finding that an addition of nuts of one sort or another renders their ale actually nut-brown without being unappetising. You can add any type of nut to pretty much any type of beer, although a filbert Pilsner is somewhat hard to imagine. The original flavour of the nut should come through whether you add it to the boil or the secondary, but nuts are not particularly aromatic and you might want to reflect that in your choice of hops. Hazelnuts, Corylus avellana, are a favourite choice, partly at least because they are the easiest to get in any quantity but mainly for their rich, deep flavour that can only really be described as 'nutty'. Like all nuts they are very oil-rich, which can flatten any chance of a good head on your beer unless you also use torrefied wheat. To get the best out of them, shell them (one at a time, sorry!) using a good old-fashioned nutcracker, and toast them in a medium oven for 10-15 minutes until the dark, bitter skin cracks and the flesh turns a pale gold. Rub the skin off and break up the nuts as you would make cracked ice – i.e., wrap them in a cloth and whack them with a hammer or rolling pin. Any nuts can be treated in the same way – almonds, pecans, macadamias, walnuts (whose inner skins are very bitter), pistachio. But you might find it simpler to buy a good extract, and peanuts are a case in point. With their thin shells and papery skins peanuts are actually the easiest of all nuts to process by hand; but many brewers are finding that peanut butter does the job just as well for a fraction of the effort – as indeed, with chestnuts (*see* above).

Heather: heather ale has become the stuff of legend thanks to the old story of the Pictish chief who died rather than divulge the recipe to the Vikings. The real mystery, though, is what Calluna vulgaris actually brings to the party. Using the flowers, new tips and a bit of twig will confer some (but hardly any) floral aroma and tannic bitterness on a brew, along with a wee bit of sugar from the nectar, while the chlorogenic acid in the stem might convey a hint of peach and green tea, although not very strongly. It has been suggested that the secret of heather beer's appeal lay not in the plant itself, but in the allegedly hallucinogenic effect of a psychotropic ergot-like fungus that clung to it. This is why if you brew with heather today without thoroughly washing it first you risk prosecution. If you still insist, though, you can spend your summer vacation picking it then use one part flowers to five parts malt in your mash; or you can add flowers, new shoots and a little bit of stem early in the boil; or you can strain your hot wort through a mat of flowers and shoots after the boil; or you can add the flowers either whole or as a tea late in the boil or to the fermenter.

Herb Bennet aka Wood Avens: the humble and almost ubiquitous woodland shrub Geum urbanum was a veritable pharmacopeia for late medieval and early modern herbalists, making a pleasant and effective digestif, a topical antiseptic, a restorative for convalescents and a salve against acne. Its other name, caryophyllata, is revealing: the root is heavily charged with eugenol, aka caryophyllic acid, the chief flavour component of the clove. The root, either fresh or dried, was often boiled or steeped in wine, and one 15th-century recipe has it suspended in a bag in the beer-barrel along with sage, rosemary and thyme. The inference is that it can be added to the boil (although in quite some quantity, as the oil's volatiles are quickly evaporated) or used as a dry hop. It also contains preservatives including tannic acid and other compounds effective against spoilage microbes such as lactobacillus and listeria.

Lavender: Lavandula angustifolia has migrated from the knicker-drawer to the kitchen in recent years for the simple reason that, used in cordials, liqueurs, sauces, sorbets, ice-creams and many other sweet drinks and desserts, it is both distinctive and delicious. Its oil composition shares a few terpenes with the hop – low levels of myrcene, caryophyllene, pinene and limonene, and quite a high farnesene level; but what really dominates is linalool. It works very well in a wheat beer or a saison and can be added sparingly at almost any point, either as flowers (fresh or dried) or as a tea or a tincture. A word of warning: use only the flowers, fresh or dried, as any lavender that has been prepared may very well contain camphor.

Lemongrass/lemon balm: Cymbopogon citratus brings a beautifully sweet lemony softness, more like the peel of a

Sorrento lemon than of the common-or-garden supermarket variety. To make something really special of a wheat beer or golden ale, lemongrass might well be preferred over genuine lemon peel because it's alkaline, not acid, and carries appreciable percentages of myrcene and geraniol. Choose the bulb rather than the tips of the leaves and soften it in boiling water before use; add late in the boil or to the fermenter. The same can be said of Melissa officinalis, a ubiquitous member of the mint family whose principal flavour component is, confusingly, called rosemarinin. Lemon balm also contains hefty doses of citral A and B and citronellal, though, as well as those familiar terpenes caryophyllene, geraniol and linalool. However, and despite the fact that lemon balm probably lines your garden path, lemongrass is much easier for most of us to source in worthwhile quantities and usable form.

Liquorice: the use of Glycyrrhiza glabra in brewing has an ancient pedigree. Like so many other herbs and roots it has long been prescribed for digestive disorders (it's quite a powerful laxative!), and it was probably first employed by brewers for its medicinal properties. But it's the natural sweetener glycyrrhizin that has the most marked effect: 50 times sweeter than sugar, it has a unique lingering quality that will give a stout or an old ale a rich, velvety mouthfeel. It also aids head retention. Add dried root at the very end of the boil to get the effect – but if you want more than just a hint of that distinctive liquorice flavour, throw in coarsely crushed star anise as well.

Meat: in the era before fermentation was understood, it was absolutely standard practice for cidermakers to restart a stuck ferment by throwing a piece of meat (or, as legend has it, a dead rat) into the vat. The nitrogen released by the decomposing meat would feed the yeast and get the fermentation going again. It has never been suggested that the same practice was used by brewers; however in the late 17th-century cookbook *The Closet of the Eminently Learned Sir Kenelm Digby Kt. Opened* we find a recipe for a nourishing broth in which a rooster was boiled to rags with various herbs and spices, thoroughly pounded and steeped for a few days in sack sherry. The strained liquor was then added to a barrel of beer and left to infuse for a couple of weeks. Whether it was any good or not Sir Kenelm does not reveal, but modern craft brewers have been busily adding not only chicken but dry-roast smoked bacon, whale bones, pan-juices of roast lamb, beef hearts, bull's testicles, pig's heads and smoked goat brains at various stages to anything from pale ales to stouts.

As with oysters, though (*see* below), the additions have only rarely been in sufficient quantity to produce a discernible flavour or aroma (the roast lamb pan-juices being, according to one who has tried it, one notable and rather bizarre exception). If trying this yourself, be sure to choose only the leanest meat, hence the need to dry-roast the bacon before use. You know without being told what lipids can do to a beer!

Mugwort: before there were hops, the leaves and roots of Artemisia vulgaris had been used by brewers from time out of mind as a bittering agent (although the mug- element more likely derives from 'muggi', Old Norse for swamp, rather than mug as in tankard). Like its near-relation wormwood, it contains small quantities of the mint-flavoured toxin thujone, which may have preservative qualities, and the very bitter-tasting absinthin as well as eucalyptol and other more pleasant-tasting volatiles. In medieval times it was considered one of the strongest of magical herbs, which could protect against enchantment and possession as well as more mundane ills. Perhaps not as effective in bittering a brew as a straightforward high-alpha hop, though!

Nutmeg: a little ball of hard woody material, nutmeg seems (as its name suggests) more like a nut than anything else. But in fact it's the fruit of an Indonesian evergreen, Myristica fragrans, and it certainly lives up to its name. The principal volatile in its essential oil is camphene, which makes up some 70 per cent and is responsible, along with a trace amount of geraniol, for the unmistakeable warm, earthy aroma. The little spicy stab in the background comes from the lesser quantities of pinene and limonene. It's often recommended that you should use it freshly grated, but coarsely pounded and added in a bag is better since it is not very soluble and will form a slick if too fine. Nutmeg is indissolubly associated with Christmas and is normally used in conjunction with other festive spices. Use sparingly or it tends to dominate.

Oysters: in recent years a number of craft brewers have revived what they believed to be a tradition of adding oysters to stout towards the end of the boil. Allegedly this practice dates back to Victorian London when both oysters and stout were cheap and fortifying working-class staples; but closer scrutiny suggests that while oysters went beautifully with stout, they never actually went in it, and that the few attempts at producing a commercial oyster stout that actually contained oysters were a flop. The shells were a different matter. Disposing of the mountains of them that

OTHER FLAVOURINGS

built up in Victorian London was quite a poser. Building 'shell grottoes' such as the world-famous one (long since destroyed, alas) at De Hems in Macclesfield Street, Soho, was one solution; using them as acidity regulators and fining agents was another. As for adding the flesh and liquor towards the end of the boil, as many craft brewers have done, well, common opinion seems to be that the almost indiscernible change to the flavour of the beer doesn't justify the expense of the fish. Modern craft brewers have substituted dried shrimp, snails and even woodlice, but without notable success.

Peanuts: *see* hazelnuts.

Rosehip: hedgefruit of all sorts have been used to flavour peasant cookery in Britain and Europe from time immemorial. Most people are familiar with blackberries, crab apples, damsons and sloes but many others – hawthorn-berry, rowanberry and rosehips in particular – seem to have slipped beneath the culinary radar. Given their versatility – they make jellies, jams, sauces, pie-fillings, country wines, cordials and even pálinka, a Hungarian and Balkan eau-de-vie – it seems a great waste to let the birds have them all. Not all are great in brewing but one, the rosehip, is beginning to attract attention partly for its massive, warm fruity and flowery aroma and partly because fresh rosehips are so easy to come by. They're also a fantastic source of Vitamin C, which means they're very acid, so watch your pH. They can be pulped and added halfway through or towards the end of the boil or to secondary, but it might be best if they're used as a cordial, since the tiny hairs that surround the seeds are an unpleasant irritant.

Sage: Salvia officinalis appears to have been one of the more widely used herbal ingredients in medieval brewing. Today it's rather like the Brussels sprouts of the herb world – it only comes out at Christmas when everybody thinks they want sage and onion stuffing, and most of it ends up choking the garbage disposal unit. To the medieval mind, though, it was a cure-all – and indeed biochemically speaking, it's a killing-ground for bugs both great and microscopic. Rich in toxins lethal to microbes and insects alike – cineole, borneol, thujone – it also carries a load of acids including tannic, oleic, ursonic, carnosic, fumaric and chlorogenic. It's an antioxidant with superfood status. And in addition it's charged with some great flavour/aroma components: caffeine, eucalyptus from the cineole, green tea and apricots from the chlorogenic acid. On top of that, it's hardy and easy to cultivate. In fact sage may well be the nearest the hop had to serious competition in the late middle ages. And now it's enjoying a revival: a number of US craft brewers have adopted it with great success, partly because of its enormous versatility. You can use it anywhere you like and combine it with a wide range of complementaries including molasses, rosemary and thyme (but not parsley!), rye, liquorice, brown sugar… and it's cheap, too. So play!

Soft fruit: strawberries, raspberries, redcurrants and many other soft fruits used either on a base of wheat beer or a very pale ale (mashed with lager malt, perhaps?) make fantastic beers for hot summer days, both tasty and refreshing even served nearly ice-cold. Raspberries in particular are very versatile: their strong flavour goes just as well with dark chocolate as white, and just as well with a brown ale or porter as a wheat beer or pale ale. They're also particular favourites in sours. But don't neglect other soft fruits: gooseberry beer, traditionally known as 'grozet', is increasingly popular; many craft brewers are using blueberries now; English brewer Charles Wells has been brewing a hugely successful banana beer for 20 years; and the tart smack of cranberries brings a brilliant balance to a sweet, full-bodied amber or brown ale. The only limit, really, on what you choose is availability and price. As well as being wonderfully tasty and aromatic, soft fruit is so easy to process and so very versatile. Fresh, frozen, chopped, mashed, puréed, as cordials, in hop-bags, late in the boil, in the secondary, even in the mash – the choice is yours.

There are a few caveats to be made, though. All soft fruits come with their own acidity, sweetness and volume as well as their flavour and aroma, and these have to be factored into your calculations. What also has to be factored in is that soft fruits mostly need to be used in large quantities and unless you can either grow your own or buy in bulk, they can be costly. There are, however, well-made natural extracts on the market that will do much the same job at a reasonable price. And finally, their colour can be extraordinarily resistant to cleaning. A well-known English family brewery, a few years ago, made a draft strawberry ale that stained the beer-lines in its 50-odd tied pubs so virulently and persistently scarlet that they all had to be replaced.

Spruce tips: *see* Conifer needles.

Stone fruit: much the same might be said of stone fruits: they run the gamut. While the heady warmth of peach can infuse a pale ale with sunshine, greengage can deepen and enrich a strong bitter or ruby ale, and plum – or even better, if you can get sufficient quantities, damson – brings a tart crispness to the most staid and stolid of porters. The only real difference between soft and fruit and stone fruit, in fact, is the stone. Most stones or pits contain cyanide – not nearly enough to hurt you, but enough to add a distinct almond flavour to your finished product that you may or may not want. Given that the stones, if added during either stage of the fermentation, will also produce a small amount of methanol, you're probably better off separating them from the pulp. Don't throw them away, though! If you're producing stone-fruit beers on any sort of scale there are people who will pay for the pits and their charges of highly prized kernel oils, or you might even want to extract the oils for your own use.

Tropical fruits: bearing in mind how glorious a ripe mango or pineapple can be on a baking hot day, it comes as a disappointment to many that so little of the refreshing character of tropical fruit carries across into beer. Commercial concoctions abound, normally made simply by adding extract to a finished beer. But whole fresh tropical fruits – kiwi, passion fruit, acai, guava, papaya, dragonfruit – have proved tricky to brew with because they have few particularly distinctive flavour compounds and their true character – their balance of sweetness and acidity – is all too easily knocked out by the beer's own flavours and aromas. Still, they're fun to play with and can enrich the body of a light summer beer: add the flesh, pulped or not, and/or the juice at secondary, and choose complementary aroma hops. Alternatively, squirt some extract into your bottling bucket!

Vanilla: the world's second most expensive spice after saffron, the seed-pod of Vanilla planifolia is still hugely in demand, which is why vanilla 'essence' is actually made of synthetic vanillin (a by-product of paper-making, believe it or not) mixed with ethanol, and you wouldn't necessarily want that in your beer! The other side of the coin is that although real vanilla pods are prohibitively expensive there are good extracts available (extracts, not essences) that are so powerful you don't need to use an awful lot. The most common use of vanilla in brewing is to aromatise stouts and porters, so choose recipes that don't require a lot of aroma hops or reduce the amount of aroma hops you use as appropriate.

Wormwood: Artemisia absinthium, the dominant flavour and aroma component of both vermouth and absinthe, is powerful stuff. The rather straggly and nondescript wayside shrub has been used for centuries to expel intestinal parasites such as the tapeworm, reduce the fever-patient's temperature and dull gastro-intestinal pain. It's also an antidepressant that induces a lasting light-headed and dreamy state, but it's now known not to be actually hallucinogenic. For the brewer, its chief use is as a preservative: its 56 chemical compounds include toxic thujone as well as tannins, flavonoids and phenols that between them are strongly antibacterial, antimicrobial and antifungal. They create a lot of bitterness too! The distinctive flavour comes chiefly from thymol aided and abetted by myrcene, humulene and caryophyllene. Use late in the boil or sparingly during secondary fermentation and, if complementing the wormwood with a bittering hop, go easy on the alphas.

Yarrow: as a genuinely strong anti-inflammatory, Achillea millefolium has been a popular herbal medicine for centuries. It makes an ointment that's good for open sores, ulcers and stubborn wounds; a poultice to aid sleep and ease pain; and a wine decoction or a tea to hasten clotting, ease haemorrhoids and relieve upper respiratory mucal discharges. The formidable battery of chemical compounds that produces all these effects includes thujone, achilleine acid and the antiseptic cineol. They also produce a terrific astringent bitterness that acts as a good preservative, and a lemony aroma with hints of chamomile possibly from the trace amount of linalool. Use the tiny flowers and feathery leaves, fresh or dried, sparingly in the boil and primary.

OTHER FLAVOURINGS

Adding Spices

Always use spices whole, never powdered. Powdered spices are insoluble and leave a scummy film that will stymie any hopes of a decent head.

If adding spices dry at whatever stage – in the mash, towards the end of the boil or in the bottling bucket or the barrel – break them up roughly and be sure to use a mesh bag. Apart from the convenience, the bag will stop chunks of nutmeg or stubborn cloves from choking your pipes.

Tinctures, or alcohol solutions, are an ideal way of extracting the flavour components from spices, needles and grasses, and are simplicity itself to prepare. Simply break your spices as above, fill a sterilised airtight jar with them, cover them with vodka or white rum and leave them for a few days to infuse, shaking and testing occasionally. When you think the tincture is strong enough, be sure to strain it very thoroughly. The great advantages of this method are that it's consistently repeatable, and at the same time it's versatile – you can always decrease or increase your addition from batch to batch.

Adding Fruit

Soft and stone fruits should be partially pulped before use, and pits and hulls should as far as possible be removed. The pulp can be added as it is, provided it's absolutely fresh; alternatively, reduce it to a purée or make it into a cordial.

A hot cordial is made by putting a bowl or bucket of the fruit into a bain-marie until the juice runs; boiling and stirring briefly; allowing to cool; then squeezing out in a muslin bag. For cold cordial, which has the truer flavour but doesn't keep, pulp the fruit and stir in a pectin enzyme; cover; leave overnight; and squeeze out as above.

In most cases, frozen fruit makes a perfectly adequate substitute for fresh; however, most suppliers also carry a variety of natural extracts.

PART THREE

... and bubble

The celebrated Bavarian Reinheitsgebot or Purity Law of 1516 decreed that beer should be brewed only from malt, hops and water. The absence of wheat from the list of permitted ingredients is taken as an implicit ban on its use, but also conspicuously absent is yeast. That doesn't mean, of course, that yeast was also banned, but it does suggest that brewers of the time regarded yeast as a process aid rather than an ingredient, just as we see isinglass today.

If so, they were wrong. Yeast cultures not only have flavours of their own, they also (as we now understand) affect the flavour components in the worts they ferment, masking some and enhancing others. Quite apart from the obvious choices of ale yeast, lager yeast or brettanomyces, the individual strain of yeast or blend of yeasts the brewer selects plays perhaps as significant a part in crafting the finished product as the malt and hops themselves.

For yeast, as you know, produces a lot more than just ethanol and CO_2. Different strains also produce other chemicals that generate different flavours. Esters taste fruity; phenols are spicy; diacetyl tastes like butterscotch. The flavours created by the yeast can complement the flavours created by your malt grist: for instance, if you're brewing a Belgian-style ale you might want those esters; if you're brewing a barley wine you might want a hint of butterscotch. They might just as easily clash, though, and we haven't even started on matching hop strains and hopping rates to different strains of yeast.

Now, a book big enough to list details of every strain of brewer's yeast in the known universe would be more than a trifle unwieldy because there are, quite literally, zillions of them – you wouldn't think, in fact, that a single-cell speck was capable of so much variation. Not only does every brewery of any size have its own house strain, zealously nurtured from generation to generation and with a spare supply safely dried or frozen in a secure yeast-bank in case of accident or infection, but (as with hops) commercial labs are continually experimenting with new strains that are faster, cleaner, more reliable, more true-to-styleand easier to handle. White Labs is also going retro: under its Yeast Vault programme it is releasing in small cultured-to-order batches many of the strains it has banked but not marketed over the last 20 years. Here we have assembled a selection of some 120 of all these many and varied strains, almost entirely from the sales catalogues of leading laboratories, which we hope constitute a representative enough sample selected across a broad enough spectrum to suit any and every purpose you might have in mind.

The same constraint applies to the amount of data that can be supplied for each entry. We have, as always, sought to provide enough to be useful, but not so much as to be encyclopaedic. We have therefore stripped the information in each listing down to what we think is a bare minimum for practical purposes. That starts with classifying the listings according to the intended usage of each strain and each strain's name with lab and order number, followed by a brief description. The attenuation value is the percentage of available sugar the strain ought to be able to process, with 72 per cent or less as low and 78 per cent or more being high. The flocculation potential is a rough indication of how efficiently the dead yeast cells will clump and sink; a low flocculation rate may cause a haze that can be fined for a brilliantly clear beer or ignored for a beer that's less brilliant but more full-bodied. Finally, the range of optimum fermentation temperatures deserves particular attention since too cool or too warm a ferment will almost certainly create off-flavours. Home-based lager brewers should also choose a strain that will work with their cooling equipment! Two details we have not included in individual listings are the format each strain is packaged in and their alcohol tolerance. We believe that brewers of your experience and expertise are more than proficient enough to handle dry and liquid packages with equal aplomb. And we have gathered all the highly tolerant strains into a classification of their own simply to make them easier to find and browse.

1: Yeasts

General ale yeasts

American Ale Yeast (Siebel BRY-96): clean ale strain. Attenuation: 78%. Flocculation: high. Brewing temperature: 64-72°F/12-22°C.

American Ale Yeast aka Chico Yeast (Wyeast 1056): versatile all-rounder. Clean, crisp and low in fruity flavours and esters.
73-77%; L-M; 60-72°F/15-22°C.

American Ale Blend (White Labs WLP060): blend of WLP001 and two other clean, neutral strains. Accentuates hop aroma and bitterness.
75-80%; M; 68-75°F/20-23°C.

American Ale II Yeast (Wyeast 1272): consistent and versatile. Slightly nutty, soft, clean and tart finish.
72-76%; M; 60-72°F/15-22°C.

American West Coast Ale Yeast (Lallemand BRY-97): very clean flavour; slightly estery aroma. A popular workhorse.
78%; M; 63°F/16°C.

Australian Ale Yeast (White Labs P009): originally from Coopers of Adelaide. Produces a clean, malty beer with bready esters. Ferments cleanly at higher temperatures.
70-75% H; 65-70°F/18-21°C.

Brewferm Top Yeast (Brewferm): extremely versatile top-fermenting yeast. Fast and efficient worker; forms fruity esters.
75%; M-H; 66-80°F/18-25°C.

British Ale Yeast (White Labs P005): originally from Whitbread. Like most English strains, it produces malty beers with a tart crispness and slight fruitiness.
67-74%; H; 65-70°F/18-21°C.

Burton Ale Yeast (White Labs P023): originates from Burton upon Trent, England's brewing capital. Creates deliciously subtle fruity flavours like apple and pear as well as clover and honey,
69-75%; M; 68-73°F/20-23°C.

California Ale V (White Labs P051): produces fruitier, fuller-bodied beers than California Ale Yeast (see Alcohol Tolerant Yeasts, below).
70-75%; M-H; 66-70°F/19-21°C.

Cream Ale Yeast Blend (White Labs P080): a blend of ale and lager strains that together create a crisp, light American ale. Generates estery aromas and moderates hop bitterness.
75-80%; M; 65-70°F/18-21°C.

Cask & Bottle Conditioning Yeast (Lallemand CBC-1): may be used in primary, but specially developed for its refermentation qualities. Will ferment up to 12% ABV and is completely flavour-neutral. Drops to form a tight mat within three days.
78%; H; 59-77°F/15-25°C.

Denny's Favorite 50 (Wyeast 1450): all-rounder named after a long-standing homebrew customer. Accentuates malt, caramel or fruit character without being too sweet.
74-76%; L; 60-70°F/15-21°C.

Dry English Ale Yeast (White Labs P007): a clean, highly flocculent and highly attenuative strain. Similar to other English strains in flavour, but more attenuative.
70-80%; M-H; 65-70°F/18-21°C.

East Coast Ale Yeast (White Labs P008): as clean as California Ale Yeast (see Alcohol Tolerant Yeasts, below), but with less attenuation, less accentuation of hop bitterness, increased flocculation and a little tartness. Low esters.
70-75%: L-M; 68-73°F/20-23°C.

Empire Ale Yeast (Mangrove Jack M15): generates rich, dark-fruit aromas and flavours. Suitable for all full-bodied ales.
70-75%; H; 64-72°F/18-22°C.

East Midlands Ale Yeast (White Labs P039): British-style ale yeast with a very dry finish. Medium to low fruit and fusel alcohol production.
73-82%; M-H; 66-70°F/19-21°C.

Edinburgh Scottish Ale Yeast (White Labs P028): everyday strain similar to California Ale Yeast (see Alcohol Tolerant Yeasts below) but not quite so alcohol resistant. Suitable for more complex and flavourful ales as it doesn't mute hop bitterness.
70-75%; M; 65-70°F/18-21°C.

English Ale Yeast (White Labs P002): classic strong bitter strain from one of England's largest independent breweries. Flocculates well to produce a brilliantly clear beer; moderate attenuation leaves some residual sweetness.
63-70%; V; 65-68°F/18-20°C.

English Ale Yeast Blend (White Labs P085): a blend of British strains designed to add complexity. Moderately fruity and minerally character, with little to no sulphur.
69-76%; M-H; 68-72°F/20-22°C.

Irish Ale Yeast (White Labs P004): originally from one of the oldest stout-producing breweries in the world (could they mean Guinness?), produces a hint of diacetyl balanced by light fruitiness and dry crispness. Ideally suited to full-bodied stouts and Scotch ales.
69-74%; M-H; 65-68°F/18-20°C.

Liberty Bell Ale Yeast (Mangrove Jack M36): fruity esters but largely neutral flavour. Helps develop malt character in all pale and golden ales.
74-78%; H; 64-73°F/18-22°C.

London Ale Yeast (White Labs P013): dry, malty ale yeast that creates a complex woody, tart, estery character with a hint of diacetyl. Hop bitterness comes through well.
67-75%; M; 66-71°F/19-22°C.

Muntons Premium Gold (Muntons): clean and well balanced; high esters, low residual sugar. Excellent crusting characteristics are helpful in cask and bottle conditioning.
75%; H; 66-72°F/19-22°C.

Muntons Standard Yeast (Muntons): popular for its consistently good performance; clean finish leaves enough residual sugars to enrich body and mouthfeel.
70%; M; 64-70°F/18-21°C.

Y
E
A
S
T
S

Northeast Ale Yeast (East Coast Yeast ECY29): a clone of the ground-breaking proprietary strain Conan, which famously accentuates the fruity and floral characters of so many American aroma hops and has a staggeringly high rate of attenuation.
78-86%; H; 65-70°F/18-21°C.

Northwest Ale Yeast (Wyeast 1332): classic ale strain from American Northwest.Malty, mildly fruity, good depth and complexity.
67-71%; H; 65-75°F/18-24°C.

Nottingham Ale Yeast (Lallemand): cultured from the house yeast of a large English commercial brewery and renowned among craft and home brewers for its consistency, its versatility – it has on occasion served as a lager yeast – and its unusually high attenuation that has been known to exceed 85 per cent. Flavour is very nearly neutral with only a hint of esters.
80-90%; H; 57-70°F/14-21°C.

Old Newark Ale Yeast (East Coast Yeast ECY10): house ale yeast from a now defunct New Jersey brewery. Good for all styles of American and English ales.
70%; H; 60-68°F/15-20°C.

Old Newark Beer Yeast (East Coast Yeast ECY12): house lager yeast from the same brewery. Has been identified as Saccharomyces cerevisiae and therefore not a lager strain, but works at lagering temperatures.
73-77%; M: 58-68°F/14-20°C.

Old Sonoma Ale (White Labs P076): neutral and versatile strain originally from a historic North California brewery; taken up by the pioneers of American craft brewing and still a popular option for traditional British-style beers especially pale ales, porters and stouts.
70-74%; M; 66-70°F/19-21°C.

Pacific Ale Yeast (White Labs P041): popular ale yeast originating from the Pacific Northwest; clears well and provides a malty, fruity profile suitable for English-style ales.
65-70%; H; 65-68°F/18-20°C.

Ringwood Ale Yeast (Wyeast 1187): English strain with distinctive fermentation and flavour characteristics. Fruity esters and maltiness create a complex profile. Flocculation is high, so the beer should fall bright without fining or filtration. Can be a slow fermenter after a long lag time.
68-72%; H; 64-74°F/18-23°C.

Safale S-04 (Fermentis): English ale yeast. Fast fermenter; good flocculation. Specially selected for cask-conditioned ales and for use in cylindro-conical fermenters.
75%; H; 59-68°F/15-20°C.

Safale US-05 (Fermentis): clean with mild flavour; produces balanced beers with low diacetyl and a crisp palate. Good head formation.
77-81%; M; 59-75°F/15-24°C.

The One (Real Brewers Yeast): very widely used California ale yeast ideal for West Coast-style pale ales and IPAs. Performs well throughout the brew – works well at high temperature; attenuates well for a clean and efficient

ferment; flocculates strongly for a bright finish.
70-80%; H; 68-75ºF/20-24ºC.

US West Coast Ale Yeast (Mangrove Jack M44): clean, neutral strain that really enhances hop character.
75-80%; M; 59-74ºF/15-24ºC.

Windsor British Ale Yeast (Lallemand): produces fruity and estery flavours. Does not ferment maltotriose, so there will be quite some residual sweetness. Suitable for all session- to mid-strength ales including wheat beers.
73-77%; L; 59-72ºF/15-22ºC.

Lager Yeasts

American Lager Yeast (White Labs P840): dry and clean with tart green-apple fruitiness. Sulphur and diacetyl production are minimal.
75-80%; M; 50-55ºF/10-12ºC.

Bavarian Lager Yeast ((Wyeast 2206): general-purpose strain used by many German breweries. Rich, full-bodied and malty.
73-77%; M-H; 46-56ºF/8-13ºC.

Bavarian Lager Yeast (Mangrove Jack M76): rounded, malty, low esters. Accentuates hop character.
78%+; M; 45-57ºF/8-14ºC.

Bohemian Lager Yeast (Wyeast 2124): probably the world's most widely used brewing yeast, with a temperature range that will even allow it to ferment ales. Lagers fermented with this strain tend to be malty and full-bodied, which is why it is used to reproduce pre-Prohibition German-style

American lagers with higher gravities and more hop bitterness than their modern counterparts.
73-77%; L-M; 46-68°F/7-20°C.

Bohemian Lager Yeast (Mangrove Jack M84): very dry and clean. Brings out noble hop characters. Suits softer, more delicate lagers.
78%+; H; 50-59°F/10-15°C.

California Lager Yeast (Mangrove Jack M54): a very useful strain that develops authentic lager characteristics at ale temperatures and conditions quickly. Clean aroma; crisp, clean mouthfeel.
77-82%; H; 64-68°F/18-20°C.

Copenhagen Lager Yeast (White Labs P850): clean, crisp northern European lager yeast. Not as malty as southern European strains.
72-78%; M; 50-58°F/10-14°C.

Cry Havoc Lager Yeast (White Labs P862): licensed from US home brewing icon Charlie Papazian, Cry Havoc will ferment at both ale and lager temperatures, allowing brewers to produce diverse beer styles.
66-70%; L; 55-58°F/13-14°C.

Czech Budejovice Lager Yeast (White Labs P802): Pilsner yeast from southern Czech Republic. Produces dry and crisp lagers with low diacetyl.
75-80%; M; 50-55°F/10-12°C.

Czech Pils Yeast (Wyeast 2278): another good choice for dry but malty Pilsners and bocks. Sulphur produced during

YEASTS

low-temperature fermentation will dissipate during conditioning.
70-74%; M-H; 50-58°F/10-14°C.

Danish Lager Yeast (Wyeast 2042): rich, yet crisp and dry. Soft, light profile accentuates hop characteristics. Particularly suited to Export-style beers such as Dortmunder.
73-77%; L; 46-56°F/7-13°C.

Diamond Lager Yeast (Lallemand): a firm favourite with brewers both amateur and commercial, and for many reasons. It's reliable, simple to use, a quick starter, a fast fermenter, very versatile and almost neutral in flavour and aroma. Low flocculation tends to mask hop bitterness a little.
77%; L; 50-60°F/10-15°C.

European Lager Yeast (Wyeast 2247): Clean, dry, mildly aromatic.
73-77%; L; 46-56°F/8-13°C.

German Bock Yeast (White Labs P833): very versatile strain from the Alps of southern Bavaria, producing balanced malt and hop character.
70-76%; M; 48-55°F/7-13°C.

German Lager Yeast (White Labs P830): malty but clean; one of the most widely used lager strains in the world.
74-79%; M; 50-55°F/10-12°C.

Mexican Lager Yeast (White Labs P940): from Mexico City, last bastion of old-style Vienna lagers, this yeast produces clean, crisp beers and suits Mexican-style light lagers as

well as the traditional darker style.
70-75%; M; 50-55°F/10-12°C.

Munich Helles Lager Yeast (White Labs P860): strong
fermenter; produces balanced malty lagers across the lager
spectrum from Munich Helles to Rauchbier.
68-72%; M; 48-52°F/9-11°C.

Munich Lager Yeast (Wyeast 2308): Attenuates well to
produce dry, smooth, full-bodied, well-rounded South
German-style lagers.
73-77%; M; 48-56°F/9-15°C.

Munich Lager Yeast II (Wyeast 2352): a genuine Munich
strain. Low diacetyl, low sulphur.
72-74%; M; 52-62°F/11-16°C.

Oktoberfest/Märzen Lager Yeast (White Labs P820): produces
a very malty, bock-like beer. Slower acting than German
Lager Yeast (see above): requires either a larger starter or a
longer lagering time.
65-73%; M; 52-58°F/11-14°C.

Old Bavarian Lager Yeast (White Labs P920): rounded and
malty; produces esters. Works well in dark lagers, Oktober-
fest biers, bocks.
66-73%; M; 50-55°F/10-15°C.

Pilsner Lager Yeast (White Labs P800): classic Pilsner strain
from the Czech Republic. Dry with a biscuity finish.
72-77%; M-H; 50-55°F/10-12°C.

Saflager S189 (Fermentis): from the former Hürlimann Brewery in Zurich, which experimented extensively with alcohol-tolerant yeasts. A fairly neutral strain allowing hop character and malt flavours to dominate.
84%; L; 54-59°F/12-15°C.

Saflager S-23 (Fermentis): from the VLB institute in Berlin. Produces an especially fruity and estery character when fermented at the bottom of its temperature range. High attenuation and flocculation create clean dryness and brilliant clarity.
82%; H; 48-60°F/9-15°C.

Saflager W34/70 (Fermentis): from Weihenstephan in Bavaria, which is claimed to be the world's oldest brewery. Clean strain that allows good balance of floral and fruity notes.
83%; H; 54-59°F/12-15°C.

San Francisco Lager (White Labs P810): will work at up to 65°F/18°C while retaining lager characteristics and is therefore the standard strain for fermenting 'California Common' or steam beer, but it will also ferment down to 50°F/10°C to produce märzens, Pilsners /other lager styles.
65-70%; H; 58-65°F/15-18°C.

Southern German Lager Yeast (White Labs P838): characterised by a malty finish and balanced aroma. Produces some sulphur but low diacetyl.
68-76%; M-H; 50-55°F/10-12°C.
Workhorse Beer Yeast (Mangrove Jack): neutral and clean aroma, works well at a wide range of temperatures and attenuates cleanly and is therefore suitable for both ales and

lagers. Good dosing strain for cask and bottle-conditioned ales.

75-80%; M; 59-68°/15-20°C.

European Ale & Saison Yeasts

Abbey IV Ale Yeast (White Labs P540): ideal for Belgian-style dubbels, trippels and specialty ales. Medium fruit character between Monastery Ale Yeast P500 (high) and Abbey Ale Yeast P530 (low).

74-82%; M; 66-72°F/19-22°C.

Belgian Abbey Ale Yeast (Mangrove Jack M47): very fruity and estery; low in phenols. Accentuates malt character.

73-77%; M; 64-77°F/18-25°C.

Belgian Ale Yeast (White Labs P550): phenolic and spicy flavours dominate the profile, with less fruit than P500.

78-85%; M; 68-78°F/20-25°C.

Belgian Ale Yeast Blend (White Labs P575): two monastery strains and a Belgian ale yeast together create a versatile blend that can be used for any Belgian style.

74-80%; M; 68-75°F/20-24°C.

Belgian Golden Ale Yeast (White Labs P570): versatile Flemish strain; a combination of fruity and phenolic characteristics dominate the flavour profile.

73-78%; L: 68-75°F/20-24°C.

Belgian Saison I Ale Yeast (White Labs P565): classic Wallonian saison yeast. Produces earthy, peppery and spicy notes. Slightly sweet.

65-75%; M; 68-75°F/20-24°C.

YEASTS

Belgian Saison II Ale Yeast (White Labs P566): more fruit and esters than P565. Moderately phenolic, with cloves in finished flavour and aroma. Ferments more quickly and consistently than WLP565.
78-85%; M; 68-78°F/20-25°C.

Belgian Strong Ale Yeast (White Labs P545): from the Ardennes, this produces moderate levels of ester and spicy phenols. Typically results in a dry but balanced finish.
78-85%; M; 68-78°F/20-25°C.

Belgian Saison Yeast Blend (White Labs P568): Belgian ale and saison strains work together to create complex fruity aromas and flavours. Phenolic, spicy, earthy and clove flavours are also notable.
70-80%; M; 70-80°F/21-26°C.

Belgian Tripel Ale Yeast (Mangrove Jack M31): brings style-appropriate dry spice, fruity esters and phenol to any Abbey or Trappist ale.
82-88%; M; 64-82°F/18-27°C.

Belgian Trappist Ale Yeast (Wyeast 3787): enhances ester and phenol character of dubbels, triples and French-style Bières de Garde.
74-78%; M; 64-78°F/18-25°C.

Düsseldorf Altbier Yeast (White Labs P036): traditional altbier yeast from Düsseldorf. Produces clean, slightly sweet altbier without affecting hop character.
65-72%; M; 65-69°F/18-20°C.

European Ale Yeast (White Labs P011): malty yeast of Bavarian origin whose low esters and negligible sulphur production give a clean profile. Low attenuation contributes to the malty character.
65-70%; M; 65-70°F/18-21°.

French Saison Ale Yeast (White Labs P590): creates farmhouse-style beers with a phenolic bite and moderate esters. Produces a clean aroma and is versatile and highly attenuating.
73-80%; M; 69-75°F/18-24°C.

Kölsch Ale Yeast (White Labs P029): originally from a small brewpub in Cologne. Accentuates hop flavours. Minimal sulphur produced during fermentation will disappear with age and leave a clean, lager-like ale.
72-78%; M: 65-69°F/18-20°C.

Monastery Ale Yeast (White Labs P500): comes from an established abbey brewer, and produces distinctive fruitiness and plum character. Fruitier and more earthy if fermented at the lower end of temperature range.
75-80%; L-M; 65-72°F/18-22°C.

Safale K-97 (Fermentis): German general-purpose ale yeast, will also ferment Belgian-style witbiers. Low esters. Strong head formation.
75%; H; 59-68°F/15-20°C.

Safale T-58 (Fermentis): develops estery and a somewhat peppery spiciness.
75%; L; 59-75°F/15-24°C.

Wheatbeer Yeasts

American Hefeweizen Ale Yeast (White Labs P320): produces slight banana and clove notes and some sulphur; otherwise clean-fermenting. Low flocculation produces a cloudy beer. 70-75%; L; 65-69ºF/18-20ºC.

Bavarian Weizen Ale Yeast (White Labs P351): produces a classic German-style hazy wheat beer with spicy phenolic overtones reminiscent of cloves. 75-77%; L; 68-70ºF/15-18ºC.

Bavarian Wheat Beer Yeast (Mangrove Jack M20): spicy aromas accompany the classic banana and clove flavours. Helps create a rich body and silky mouthfeel. 70-75%; L; 64-86ºF/18-30ºC.

Belgian Wit Ale Yeast (White Labs P400): the original witbier strain. Tart, fruity and phenolic. 74-78%, L-M; 67-74ºF/19-23ºC.

Belgian Wit II Ale Yeast (White Labs P410): less phenolic,sweeter and spicier than P400. Flocculation is superior to that of P400. 70-75%; L-M; 65-72ºF/18-22ºC.

Belgian Wit Beer Yeast (Mangrove Jack M21): generates balanced esters and phenols with a hint of bubblegum aroma; fruity flavours; some residual sweetness. Very slow to drop. 70-75%; M; 64-77ºF/18-25ºC.

Hefeweizen Ale Yeast (White Labs P300): this traditional strain produces the sought-after banana and clove notes

and authentic cloudy look in German wheat beers.
72-76%; L; 68-72°F/20-22°C.

Hefeweizen IV Ale Yeast (White Labs P380): phenolic clove aroma and flavour, with minimal banana. Also produces refreshing citrus and apricot notes for a crisp, drinkable hefeweizen. Less flocculant than P300, and sulphur production is higher.
73-80%; L; 66-70°F/19-21°C.

Munich Wheat Beer Yeast (Lallemand): Bavarian strain producing all the right clove and banana flavours and aromas. Suits all session- to mid-strength wheats.
73-80%; L; 63-76°F/17-24°C.

Munich Classic Wheat Beer Yeast (Lallemand): cultured from a strain held in the Doemens Academy collection in Munich. Particularly suited to fuller and rounder interpretations of the style thanks to its lack of flocculation. Quick starter and fast worker.
73-77%; non-flocculant; 55-66°F/13-19°C.

Safale WB-06 (Fermentis): for dry and hazy wheatbeers. Very subtle esters and phenols.
80%; L; 64-75°F/18-24°C.

Weihenstephan Weizen Yeast (Wyeast 3068): creates the distinctive phenolic clove and ester banana character of wheat beers. Very fast starter, vigorous fermenter. The low flocculation of this yeast leaves the beer cloudy.
73-77; L; 64-75°F/18-24°C.

Y
E
A
S
T
S

Alcohol-Tolerant Yeasts

Abbaye Ale Yeast (Lallemand): complex flavours produced by this strain include pepper, fruit, cloves and bananas. Suitable for all high-gravity Belgian styles.
73-77%; L; 63-74°F/17-23°C.

Abbey Ale Yeast (White Labs P530): similar to Monastery Ale Yeast P500, but less fruity. Tolerant up to 15% ABV.
75-80%; M-H; 66-72°F/19-22°C.

Bastogne Belgian Ale Yeast (White Labs P510): produces dry beer with a slight acidic finish. Clean fermentation character. Not over-spicy.
74-80%; M; 66-72°F/19-22°C.

Belgian Abbey Ale Yeast (Wyeast 1214): suitable for all high-gravity ales up to 12% ABV, especially dubbels and tripels. Estery and spicy. Can be a slow starter.
72-76%; M; 68-78°F/20-25°C.

Belgian Ale Yeast (Mangrove Jack M41): spicy and phenolic; intense and complex. Aromas of dark fruit; classic wheat beer flavours. Highly alcohol tolerant.
82-88%; M; 64-82°F/18-27°C.

Belgian Ardennes Ales Yeast (Wyeast 3522): yields mild fruit esters and complex spices; also phenolic notes if fermented at high temperature. Good flocculation makes for brilliant clarity. Tolerant up to 12% ABV or more.
72-76; H; 65-85°F/18-29°C.

Belle Saison Ale Yeast (Lallemand): high esters and phenols produce strong peppery, fruity and spicy flavours and

aromas. Fast acting; ferments up to 14% ABV. Good for French-style Bières de Garde as well as saisons and strong Belgian-style ales.
78-90%; H; 59-65°F/15-18°C.

California Ale Yeast (White Labs P001): White Labs' classic best seller, famous for its clean flavours that accentuate hop character. High alcohol tolerance and attenuation make it a great all-rounder.
73-80%; M; 68-73°F/20-22°C.

French Saison Ale Yeast (Wyeast 3711): carries peppery, spicy and citrusy notes; enhances aroma hops and spices and creates a silky mouthfeel. Tolerant to 12% ABV.
77-83%; L; 65-77°F/18-25°C.

French Saison Ale Yeast (Mangrove Jack M29): dry, warming, strongly spicy and peppery – may overwhelm hops! Highly attenuative; alcohol tolerant to 14% ABV.
85-90; M; 79-90°F/26-32°C.

Hella Bock Lager Yeast (Wyeast 2487): Austrian strain for very full-bodied, malty lagers and bockbiers. Ferments up to 12% ABV.
70-74%; M; 48-56°F/9-13°C.

Lucky #7 (Real Brewer's Yeast): Southern California ale yeast that ferments higher gravity worts up to 10% ABV. Dry and fairly neutral, but with hints of plum and vine fruit.
70-80%; H; 68-75°F/20-24°C.

Neutral Grain Yeast (White Labs P078): clean, fast-fermenting, efficient yeast intended for use in high-gravity beers. Often

The Craft Brewers' Compendium

used to ferment washes intended for distillation.
77-84%; M; 76-85ºF/24-29ºC.

New World Strong Ale Yeast (Mangrove Jack M42): suited to strong dark beers of all sorts. Neutral aroma lets hops shine through. 77-82%; V-H; 61-72ºF/16-22ºC.

Safale B-256 (Fermentis): very fast-fermenting alcohol-tolerant ale yeast selected with Abbey-style beers in mind. Produces subtle and well-balanced aromas.
82%; H; 59-68ºF/15-20ºC.

Safale S-33 (Fermentis): general-purpose and fairly neutral alcohol-tolerant ale strain selected for high-gravity speciality beers. Low attenuation and flocculation will help create a rich, rounded beer with plenty of mouthcoating and a long finish.
70%; L; 59-68ºF/15-20ºC.

San Diego Super Ale Yeast (White Labs P090): clean, fast-fermenting strain. Low esters and neutral flavour and aroma profiles make for a very versatile strain suitable for a wide range of styles.
76-83%: M-H; 65-68ºF/18-20ºC.

Super High Gravity Ale Yeast (White Labs P099): originally from England, this yeast can ferment up to 25% ABV when correctly used. Malt character dominates at lower gravities; ester character intensifies with increasing strength.
>80%; M; 65-68ºF/18-20ºC.

Turbo Yeasts: these are blends of very pure yeast strains, yeast nutrients and acidity regulators that were originally intended to ferment clean, fast, high-gravity washes for the distilling industry. There are many brands on the market: some will ferment a sugar solution up to around 14% ABV in a couple of days; others will ferment the same solution to 20 per cent or more in less than a week. How suitable they are for beer brewing is a matter for lively debate; but a third variant is very tolerant of high temperatures and is a boon to small breweries in hot climates.

Zurich Lager Yeast (White Labs P885): developed from the Hurlimann strain that once produced the celebrated 14% ABV Samichlaus Christmas beer. Can ferment lagers over 11% ABV. Sulphur and diacetyl production are minimal. 70-80%; M; 50-55°F/10-12°C.

2: Souring Agents

The brewing of sour beers of various kinds was until only a few years ago largely confined to their traditional places of origin. The biochemistry behind these antique beverages was thought too arcane for the humble home brewer to attempt, and the finished products themselves too specialised for any commercial brewer to make a viable proposition of.

But the mixture of the inquisitive and the indomitable that is the foundation of modern craft brewing has seen to it that sours are today perfect commonplaces in the brewer's repertoire and that the lactobacilli Delbrueckii, a probiotic also used in the production of yogurt, and Pediococcus, more usually found fermenting sauerkraut and farm silage, are easily obtainable by brewers around the world. Although lactobacilli aren't yeast, they are made up as a starter with sugar or DME and normally pitched during or immediately after the primary fermentation. They digest simple sugars to give off lactic acid, which is what gives the beers their tang. As bacteria, they don't produce alcohol: in fact by competing with yeast for simple sugars they can actually reduce the strength of the beer – Bremer and Berliner Weisse are commonly only 2-3% ABV.

The lambic brewers of Payottenland in Belgium not only use open fermenters, in which they are not unique, they also throw open the louvred roofs of their breweries to let passing microbes in. The precise ecology of each brewery is different, and the brewers themselves refuse to change a thing because (like some whisky distillers) they claim not to know what's lurking there and what it does, and so they are loath to upset the balance of an ecosystem of microflora and microfauna that has evolved naturally. But whatever's hiding in the undergrowth of each brewery's jungle, the king of the Belgian beasts is a yeast strain, either Brettanomyces bruxellensis or Brettanomyces lambicus, which are available to buy.

Both Lactobacilli and Brettanomyces are very slow developers, so brewing sour beers is not for the hasty. The gestation period of a Brettanomyces-based beer is generally eight or nine months, and it can take anything up to 18 months before they're ready to bottle. On the other hand they keep well and can be perfectly good after years in bottle.

> **American Farmhouse Blend (White Labs P670):** blends a traditional farmhouse yeast strain and Brettanomyces to create a complex flavour profile with a moderate level of sourness.
> 75-82%; M; 68-72°F/20-22°C.

> **Belgian Sour Mix I (White Labs P655):** blends Brettanomyces and Saccharomyces yeasts and the bacterial strains Lactobacillus and Pediococcus.
> 70-80%; L-M; 80-85°F/26-29°C.

> **Berliner Weisse Blend (White Labs P630):** a traditional German weizen yeast blended with Lactobacillus to create a subtle tartness. Can take several months to develop.
> 73-80%; M; 68-72°F/20-22°C.

Brettanomyces Bruxellensis Trois Vrai (White Labs P648): famous for its robust, complex and sour character and aromas of pear. Best used as a primary fermentation strain. 85%+; L; 70-85°F/21-29°C.

Brettanomyces bruxellensis (White Labs P650): typically used during secondary fermentation of Belgian-style sour beers and lambics to generate medium-intensity Brettanomyces character. 85%+; L; 85°F+/29°C+.

Brettanomyces claussenii (White Labs P645): originally isolated from strong English stock ale, this yeast has low-intensity Brettanomyces character and is closely related to B. Anomalus. Produces fruity, pineapple-like aroma but not such a distinctive flavour. 70-85%; L; 85°F+/29°C+.

Brettanomyces lambicus (White Labs P653): high-intensity Brettanomyces character of horsey, smoky and spicy flavours. Found most often in lambic beers as well as sour brown and red ales. 70-85%; L; 85°F+/29°C.

Flemish Ale Blend (White Labs P665): a blend of Saccharomyces and Brettanomyces yeasts with Lactobacillus and Pediococcus bacteria; this culture creates a more complex, dark stone fruit characteristic than P655. 80-85%; L-M; 68-80°F/20-26°C.

Lactobacillus brevis (White Labs P672): rod-shaped Lactobacillus used for souring. Typically produces more lactic acid than Lactobacillus Delbrueckii. 80%; L; 70-75°F/21-24°C.

Lactobacillus delbrueckii (White Labs P677): produces moderate levels of acidity and sour flavours found in lambics, Berliner Weisse, sour brown ales and gueuzes. 75-82%; L; 70-75°F/21-24°C.

Pediococcus damnosus (White Labs P661): cocci bacteria known for its lactic acid production. Slow growing and a high diacetyl producer. 65%; L; 70-75°F/21-24°C.

Saccharomyces bruxellensis trois (White Labs P644): produces a slightly tart beer with delicate mango and pineapple characteristics. Can also be used to add sparkle when bottle conditioning. Ferments more quickly than typical Brettanomyces strains. 85%+; L; 70-85°F/21-29°C.

3: Process Aids

Not everything that goes into the beer counts as an ingredient. Many are the chemical tweaks and adjustments that have to be made throughout the brewing process to ensure correct pH, to stop the mash sticking and to polish the beer to a brilliant clarity. Listed here are some of the process aids that should be found in every brewer's pantry.

Acidity regulators: calcium bicarbonate (chalk) and calcium sulphate (gypsum) should be used not only to 'Burtonise' all brewing liquor before use, they should also be on hand to correct the pH value throughout the entire process. Use either litmus paper or a pH meter and add gypsum to increase pH or chalk to reduce it accordingly.

PROCESS AIDS

Beech curls: to cut conditioning time when making Budweiser, Anheuser-Busch floats lengths of beechwood, boiled in baking soda for several hours, in the beer. Instead of sinking to the bottom in a clump the yeast cells coat the surface of the wood, increasing the contact area between yeast and beer and thus making the yeast work more efficiently and quickly. They use beechwood because it's low in resins and doesn't affect the beer's flavour. On a more modest scale, beechwood curls dunked in a grain bag into the secondary fermenter will similarly brighten and polish the beer before bottling or kegging.

Bentonite: volcanic clay usually sold in powdered form and much used as a cosmetic face pack. Bentonite's fine particles carry a strong negative charge and, when sprinkled on the surface of a conditioning tank, will collect haze-producing particles as they slowly sink. However Bentonite is not really a substitute for animal-derived finings as it collects only protein particles, not yeast cells. It can also be rather messy!

Cereal hulls: added to the mash, oat and rice hulls help prevent it from settling and sticking during the sparge. This is very helpful when mashing wheat or rye beers with a low percentage of barley malt and consequently an inadequate supply of barley husks. Rinse thoroughly before use.

Iodine: used to ensure that mash conversion is proceeding satisfactorily. A few drops of wort are squirted on to a white plate and allowed to cool, then mixed with a couple of drops of the iodine (or potassium iodine) solution. A strong dark blue/black colour indicates the presence of starch; reddish-brown shows dextrin; and clear yellow indicates that the starches have been successfully converted.

Irish moss: a polysaccharide derived from Chondrus crispus, euchema and other seaweeds which can be added a few minutes before the end of the boil to aid protein flocculation. Irish moss comes in tablet, powder and granule forms; well-known brands include Whirlfloc and Protofloc. Also known as copper finings and kettle finings.

Isinglass and other natural collagens: fining is the process of clearing the beer of microscopic yeast particles by adding an agent such as natural collagen – either isinglass, which is derived from the swim-bladders of fish, or unflavoured gelatine. Isinglass is positively charged and attracts the negatively charged yeast particles as it slowly settles through the beer. Gelatine is easier to use but less effective, with only about a tenth of the power of isinglass. A problem with using either agent is that as they're both animal derivatives, vegetarians won't (or shouldn't!) drink a beer in which they have been used. It has been proven during allergenic research that very little, if any, isinglass remains in a properly fined pint. Nevertheless, a fish had to give its life so that beer might sparkle, and many people feel that the result wasn't worth the slaughter (although as isinglass is a by-product, not using it won't save a single fishy life: it'll just mean that fishermen get less for their catch). There are no vegetarian alternatives, although given time yeast haze should clear by itself.

Oak chips: the use of oak chips, curls or cubes to mimic the effect of storage in oak barrels seems to have been adopted from high-tech winemakers, who first started infusing white wines that were actually being held in temperature-controlled stainless steel vats with old barrel-staves many years ago. How you feel about this up to you, but it is now quite common practice in brewing and you can even buy ground-

PROCESS AIDS

up bourbon casks, sherry casks and other pre-used staves.

PVPP: polyvinylpolypyrrolidone, to give it its full name (or Polyclar, to give it its most familiar brand-name), was first used in the wine industry to remove surplus tannins by agglomeration and precipitation. Added either late in the boil or to the whirlpool, it is used by brewers to precipitate polyphenols and thus reduce foaming.

Silicon: anti-foaming agents are generally food-grade silicon powders or gels that help prevent boilovers in the copper. They also speed up the coagulation of proteins in the wort, thereby reducing boiling time by as much as a third.

Sulphite: the two metabisulphites, sodium and potassium, are every brewer's first choice of cleaner and sanitiser. They kill virtually everything they touch and can therefore be used in small quantities as a preservative in bottling and kegging.

Yeast nutrient: sugar is yeast's delight, but refined sugars lack the trace minerals that our little fungal friend also requires. Full mash and all-malt extracts can supply everything the cells need to reproduce, but any recipe that calls for additional white sugar or corn syrup – and this includes some kits – will leave the yeast hungry for nitrogen, amino acids, zinc, magnesium and other minerals. These deficiencies are often the cause of stuck ferments, but home brew suppliers all stock proprietary brands of yeast nutrient: use as instructed on the packet.

Champagne & Baker's Yeasts

A few years ago there was a vogue for brewing with Champagne yeast prompted, a cynic might suppose, by the realisation that if you put almost any liquid into a wire-caged pressure bottle and add the word 'Champagne' to the label, your product will command a fantastic premium.

In practical terms, though, Champagne yeast is not all it's cracked up to be. It's alcohol-tolerant up to 15% ABV or more, but it's not highly attenuative and can't ferment maltotriose (which will make up 10-15 per cent of the fermentable sugar in most worts) at all. If you tried to ferment a beer entirely with Champagne yeast, therefore, it would not be the crisp, brut beverage you were expecting but something rather sweet and bready. Certainly it can be and is used in the secondary and in bottle conditioning, but you have to start off with a good old-fashioned beer yeast chomping its way through the maltotriose. Beer writers were, by and large, greatly appreciative of the various Champagne beers that came on the market. But few if any of them could identify specifically what it was that Champagne yeast (or, indeed, in those cases where it was adopted, the méthode champenoise) actually brought to the party – apart, that is, from the name.

Breadiness is also, perhaps predictably, the flavour most often associated with beer brewed with baker's yeast. Brewer's and baker's yeasts are the closest of relatives – brother and sister, no less – but brother and sister who have, over the years, grown apart. They have been selected for different properties, so baker's yeast is highly attenuative because it has to generate enough CO_2 to raise all that sticky gluten. As we know, fermentation produces CO_2 and alcohol in equal measure, and during the proving process a lump of dough produces a significant quantity of ethanol that is almost all evaporated during baking. This does mean, though, that baker's yeast is very alcohol-tolerant – up to 15% ABV by some accounts, although at that level of attenuation it is also reported to produce some horrible off-flavours, and 5-6% ABV is reckoned by many of those who have tried it to be its highest feasible level. And it has not been selected to flocculate because clarity is not one of the more important attributes of a loaf of bread. In sum, baker's yeast is a more practical brewing proposition than Champagne yeast, but unless you are brewing a special for a bakers' convention, say, or for the wedding of a baker's daughter, why take the trouble? Or perhaps your Baker's Daughter's Wedding Ale might use baker's yeast for the primary and Champagne yeast in the conditioning? Just the beer to toast the bride with!

A Culture of Your Own

Many winemakers, cidermakers and even whisky distillers aim for and achieve total self-sufficiency. Only a handful of brewers can make the same boast. But even if you don't have rolling acres of golden barley or endless rows of lofty bines to call your own, you can be self-sufficient in yeast. It doesn't take much space and it's not even particularly challenging to become a yeast rancher, and developing and maintaining your own culture is no mere gimmick or indulgence, either: it could easily become your signature.

A brewery produces far more yeast than it uses, and there's no reason why the excess shouldn't be carried forward to future brews. To take advantage of nature's obliging generosity simply scoop some of the kraüsen, or thick creamy foam, off the top of the primary using a slotted spoon and half-fill a sanitised jar with a wide mouth and a tight-fitting lid.

An alternative source of suitable yeast is the sediment left in the fermenter after racking. Top up the jar with cool distilled water, give it a good swirl and let the trub or lees of unwanted fats, proteins and hop matter sink to the bottom. Carefully decant the cloudy, yeasty water into another sanitised jar and repeat until you are left with a hazy liquid and little or no trub.

Let the living least cells settle into a whitish layer and store the separated liquid in the bottom of the fridge until you need it. It will keep for a month or two, darkening slightly as it ages. To use, carefully pour off the water and start the yeast in the usual way.

Meanwhile, don't throw the rest of your surplus yeast away. Pigs adore it. You can bake with it. You can boil it low and slow for hours and hours with some salt and the water in which onion, carrot, celery and turnip have been boiled to make your own vitamin-rich yeast extract spread. Or you can just drink it.

If you order a beer at the De Koninck Brewery tap in Antwerp they'll give you a shot-glass of yeast with it. You can take this home to bake with (the tradition's original purpose), you can down it by itself for its B vitamins, slight coffee flavour and mild laxative effect or you can simply tip it into your bolleke to enhance the body and enrich the flavour of the beer.

The Craft Distillers' Handbook

A practical guide to the making and marketing of spirits

Ted Bruning

"This is a brilliant book for those seeking to know what running a distillery entails and how to get started"

Alex Davies, Head Distiller, Kyoto Distillery, Japan

- Microdistilling has never been more popular. The number of gin distilleries alone, opening in the UK in 2016, was 45 with gin sales now reaching £1 billion.
- A very practical guide with 10 case studies of those who have started their own distilleries.
- Get inside information on developing the necessary skills, calculating the finances and finding the right premises.
- Find out what equipment you'll need, where to get it – and how much you would pay!
- Formulate and market your own brand of top-quality spirits and liqueurs.
- **£10.95 plus postage and packing**

www.posthousepublishing.com

The Winegrowers' Handbook

A practical guide to setting up a vineyard and winery in the UK

Belinda Kemp & Emma Rice

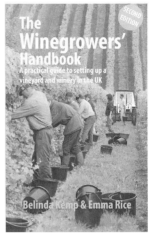

PUBLISHING Spring 2018

- FREE COPY OF THE VINEYARDS MAP OF ENGLAND AND WALES
- The most comprehensive and up-to-date guide on the market
- Written by Belinda Kemp, (Brock University Cool Climate Oenology and Viticulture Institute) and Emma Rice, Director of Wine at Hattingley Valley
- The essential commercial and business manual for potential vineyard owners and winemakers in UK
- Packed with anecdotes and case studies of people who have set up their own vineyards in UK
- Directories of useful websites, government regulations, vineyards, service providers and equipment manufacturers
- Now in its second edition and completely updated and revised
- **£10.95 plus postage and packing**

www.posthousepublishing.com

Let Me Tell Tell You About Whisky

By Neil Ridley & Gavin D. Smith

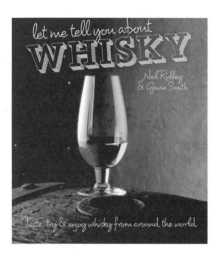

- The best whisky primer on the market
- No jargon. No snobbery and no previous knowledge assumed
- Practical details – choose, buy, serve and taste whisky with confidence
- Over 200 recommended whiskies to try from around the world with original tasting notes
- **£17.99 plus p&p**

Whisky is the world's favourite spirit and is enjoying booming sales, especially in the USA and Asia, yet too often it's shrouded in mystery, myth and complex sounding terminology. This authoritative beginner's guide cuts straight through all of this, with simple advice on how to seek out and enjoy the immense diversity of flavours and styles on offer.

The book covers not just famous Highland malts, Irish pot still whiskeys and American Bourbons, but also whiskies from South East Asia, Japan and Canada, as well as whiskies from many other producing countries, ranging from Wales through to Taiwan. There is advice on how to nose, taste and savour, how to organise a whisky tasting, which glassware to use, as well as a selection of classic whisky cocktails and advice on matching food and whisky.

This is a true beginner's guide providing a clear insight into the modern world of whisky in away that's never been done before.

www.posthousepublishing.com